THE BRIDP

POETRY, SHORT STORIE

JUDGES
Wendy Cope • Poetry
Michèle Roberts • Short Stories
David Swann • Flash Fiction

First published in 2013 by Redcliffe Press Ltd
81g Pembroke Road, Bristol BS8 3EA

e: info@redcliffepress.co.uk
www.redcliffepress.co.uk
Follow us on Twitter @RedcliffePress

Follow The Bridport Prize:
Follow us on Twitter @BridportPrize
www.bridportprize.org.uk
www.facebook.com/bridportprize

ISBN 978-1-908326-50-8

British Library Cataloguing-in-Publication Data
A catalogue record for this book is available from the British Library

Typeset in 10.5pt Times

Typeset by Addison Print Ltd, Northampton
Printed by Hobbs the Printers Ltd, Totton

Contents

MICHÈLE ROBERTS

Short Story Report

It would not have been possible for me to carry out the final judging had it not been for the hard work and professional expertise of Frances Everitt and all the team running the Bridport Prize. Thank you. I should also like to thank all the writers whose work I read.

The top three prizewinners were easy to pick. Their stories stood out immediately, characterized first and foremost by energetic, inventive language, and also by a subtle take on subject matter and themes. 'A Man in Three Moments' by Eve Thomson brilliantly telescoped time and dealt with the mysterious meanings of the word 'beauty'. 'TXL' by Kerry Hood embodied pain, difficulty, triumph and humour. 'Oyster Woman' by Sheila Crawford evoked trauma through reticence and understatement.

Twenty other stories shifted between piles labelled yes; yes/perhaps; and perhaps. Narrowing these down to ten highly commended was difficult and intriguing.

No subject is inherently interesting or boring: the writer makes it so. A lot of the stories dealt with death, or loss, or domestic life, or life on the range. The successful ones exhilaratingly made these classic subjects fresh and new, perhaps by looking at them from new or unexpected angles. Tell all the truth, but tell it slant. Emily Dickinson's words apply to fiction as much as to poetry.

I looked for excellent writing, at the level of sentence by sentence; simultaneously for writing that best expressed and invented and shaped its subject. Language is, and makes, form. I looked also for stories whose endings really worked, whether shocking or downbeat.

Nearly all the stories I read were set in the contemporary present, and many of them employed the present tense. How conscious a choice was this? Sometimes the past tense would have been helpful, allowing for narrative hindsight and irony. A lot of the stories sounded the same, employing realism or naturalism manifested through a chatty vernacular aping the speaking voice. This has to be done well, otherwise ends up sounding as loose, dull and flat as speech sometimes does. Writing is not

5

the same as talking. It employs art, often craftily and subtly concealed. Too many of the stories aped memoir, or journalism. Is this a fashion in creative writing classes? I do not know. Perhaps reality TV has become a model. This style of writing meant that experimentation was avoided, risks not taken, the imagination and the unconscious not explored, feeling not translated into image. Many of the writers seemed scared of exploring emotion, and opted instead for sounding cool, keeping a distance. This could feel like simple repression, and be dull for the reader.

I admired and enjoyed many of the stories. The best of them suggested that the writer had got close to her or his subject, lived with it for a bit, let it ferment for a while, been so affected by it that they had necessarily invented a new short story form, new arrangements of language, found the best possible narrative perspective whether close up or further away.

The fact that thousands of writers entered the competition shows how the short story form thrives. This is very encouraging, despite some publishers asserting that short stories do not do well. I am grateful to have had the chance to read the stories I did. Thank you again.

WENDY COPE

Poetry Report

It was helpful to have nearly a month between the arrival of the poems and the deadline for results. I read all of them as soon as possible and re-read them at intervals, gradually reducing the pile of possible winners. During those weeks I found that certain poems came to mind when I was going about my everyday business or just sitting quietly with a cup of tea. They were memorable. I enjoyed thinking about them and looked forward to reading them again.

'The Opposite of Dave' made me laugh out loud the first time I read it and smile every time I thought of it. They say that funny poems don't win competitions. Well, this one did. But it isn't just a funny poem. It is saying something about women and their relationships with men that many readers will find recognisable. It builds up very well to its surprise ending. You start off believing that the author is praising Dave's successor. You begin to think he doesn't sound all that great. Does she really rate this guy? And then you get the laugh.

'The Sellotape Factory' also worked its way towards the top of the pile because I found myself thinking about it so often, remembering the image of the children with their faces pressed against the wire fence, the 'nice men in overalls', who bowled them rolls of tape. But what I most admire about this poem is its author's control of tone. The anger in the poem is quiet anger, and when the poet turns the tables on the offending parents, that is done quietly too. The poem doesn't shriek and beat its breast. Some of the less successful entrants put me off by being too intense and dramatic.

'The Restaurant' is a very short poem. Like funny poems, very short ones tend not to win competitions, though I don't see any reason why they shouldn't, if they are good enough, and this one certainly is. One thinks, of course, of Larkin: 'Our almost instinct almost true: / What will survive of us is love'. Here, what survives of Christopher's father is something much more specific and mundane. But it seems to me that the poem is saying something that is both interesting and true – and saying it very well.

Although it wasn't too difficult to pick those three winners, I did have trouble getting the list of runners-up down to ten. There were too many good ones – the ten who made it had stiff competition. I can't go into detail about all of them but I would like to mention 'Rimbaud' because there were very few entries that used traditional forms and this is an excellent sonnet. Another strong contender for a top prize was 'I Left My Hair in San Francisco' because the poem, written in the voice of the hairdresser, is memorably amusing. Several of the ten poems are about old age, death or bereavement: 'Vegetable Patch', 'Unravelling', 'On My Grandmother's Bench', 'Vigil'. The last of these is written entirely in lower case letters and I have to confess I find this irritating. It is, none the less, a moving and successful poem and might have done even better if the author hadn't abandoned capitals.

There is always an element of luck in competitions. All judges have quirks and prejudices and their experiences of life will inevitably cause them to warm more to some poems than to others. The author of 'The Veranda' benefitted from the fact that I, too, have worked with children and I found the description of going on an outing – the 'combination of boredom and vigilance' – spot on.

Yes, there's an element of luck and a different judge might have made different choices. What matters, I believe, is that good poems win and I hope you'll agree that this has happened here. There will almost always be other good poems that didn't – and there were quite a few in this case. I hope their authors won't give up. I could make a long list of the competitions I didn't win before I gave up entering them. But they are one way for talented poets to gain attention and encouragement. As I write this I still don't know the names of the winners but I soon will – and I'll look out for them in future.

DAVID SWANN

Flash Fiction Report

Fans of the Marx Brothers will maybe recall the famous scene in which Groucho is allocated a tiny cabin on a transatlantic liner. For the next ten minutes, the cabin is invaded by an army of crew-members and hangers-on, until that cramped little space is teeming with people. Meanwhile, above their heads, Harpo sleeps on peacefully, borne aloft by the swarm.

I often think of that image when sitting down to write flash fiction. Ideally, the reader will float above the throng like Harpo, unaware of the chaos below. But how does the writer achieve that conjuring trick? With only 250 words at his/her disposal, there's no room for clutter. The challenge is to include everything essential, and to kick out the rest. And then to leave a space on the page for the reader.

Choosing six of the best from a shortlist of 50 proved to be a difficult task. As the first reader Jon Wyatt noted, flash fiction is easily exposed. One wrong word can tilt the whole piece out of balance. But technical deficiencies count for less when a piece achieves the 'accuracy of emotion' that Margaret Atwood once described.

In living with the shortlist for three weeks, I was interested to see how pieces rose and fell (and rose and fell again) in my affections as I read and re-read them. Ultimately, I decided that the stories I chose would be the ones that went on haunting me even after the first hit had worn off.

Like all good literature, flash fiction tends to lose its fizz when reduced to jokes or anecdotes. And it can be cruel towards over-compression and gimmicks. But the 50 writers on this year's shortlist prove what a flexible and fascinating form the micro-story remains. As well as supernatural yarns, contemporary Zen koans, and urban folk tales, I read pieces that used surrealism, magic realism, and comedy. Some of the pieces limited themselves to individual scenes, and others roamed around through time and space. Many of the stories found mystery in commonplace props and places, while others dug into rich and rewarding characters. And in the best experimental pieces, writers opened up a fascinating third space, located somewhere between fiction and poetry.

The six stories that haunted me hardest and longest were 'Polio', 'Fine', 'Locked In', 'Ern Kiley's House', 'Lincolnshire', and 'The Edge of the Woods'. Other writers would have made different choices, but these were pieces that prickled my skin as well as stimulating my admiration and envy. The following stories pushed them very close: 'Consent', 'Repo Day', 'Akira and the Creative Process', 'The Slow Acts', 'Ovid on the Train to Tomis', 'Dad's Cap', and 'Breakdown'.

I hope that all of the writers on this year's shortlist will appreciate how well they did in rising through a record pile of 2,720 entries.

EVE THOMSON

A Man in Three Moments

I

'Come up for a nightcap,' he says.

'Golly, it's late,' I say.

'Just one,' he says, smiling, head pitched to one side. 'Mm?'

It is such a quandary, a moral dilemma, and well, how is my underwear? But here he is, famous, and focused on me, on a winter city street, in the dark, below zero. The collar of his dark cashmere coat is pulled up about his ears. Just the collar, I bet, would cover my whole transatlantic ticket, return even. He reaches out and strokes my arm with a leather finger, right up the moth-eaten tweed, and cool into the neckline beneath my scarf, wound round and round. In goes a bolt of frigid air. He smiles. His teeth glint, slightly out of line, a few too many, like in the photos. Our breath comes out in white clouds, lit up by his lobby door. Through the glass I see the doorman, in a grey uniform, with gold braiding, I'm pretty sure.

We stand side by side in the lift, not touching, quiet, like a father and daughter, maybe, home from a bit of cultural bonding. The light's lovely in here, forgiving. You wouldn't imagine my coat, caught in snatches in the polished brasses, has a ripped lining. He looks down at me, paternally, nearly. And I'm wishing I'd read his books more carefully, his pieces of criticism and commentary, and could dazzle, over this drink, with my eloquence and pithy counter-arguments, with my grip on his *oeuvre*, the historical perspective – of which there is a lot, years and years and years of it, multi-translated, way back into the mists of time. And I'm trying hard to picture us, across two facing sofas, in a book-lined room, with Thelonious Monk playing in the background, maybe, and our meeting of minds. But I'm not so deluded, even at twenty-two.

He has his key in the lock. He pushes the door wide open, and gestures me inside with a courteous long sweep of an arm. In the dark I glimpse the polished parquet, and a deep view through, and two rectangles of window far off in muted night violet, and lumpy bits of furniture making blocky shapes. And then my back is up against the wall and his tongue is in my mouth, practically down my throat. He has slipped his own coat off, effortlessly, and now he's having a go at mine, and it's the ripped coat lining that's uppermost in my mind, and the shame of it. And I'm hoping there's not a light switch handy, because he's having a job with the buttons in the dark, although he'll have done this a million times in his life, blind, backwards, one-handed, through decades of fashion and quirks of fastenings, out of his head drunk or stoned, with half a mind, even, as he commits his next commentary to memory. The trouble is, I replaced the buttons, to make the coat look, you know, a bit fresher, for its second life around, and the buttons are a little bigger than the holes. I want to explain this, lightly, with a carefree laugh, but at the moment words aren't what we're doing.

He has squeezed a couple of buttons through. He's taking a faster route now, pulling the coat down over my shoulders, and I hear it fall, cold, damp, heavy, too old and knackered for this lark, to the floor. I step out of it, and we're on the move, into the inner sanctum, and the place is hermetically sealed it seems, the silence thick and soft and solid, except for his breathing in my ear *gorgeous gorgeous*. Which, I must say, is a bit creepy. Instead, I focus on the side of his neck, where my nose is now pressed, and the smell of him which is quite a thrill, blimey, although I doubt it's a plain old thrill but one all tied up with status, excellence, celebrity, and my astonishing participation in it. And I'm walking backwards and letting him guide me through the black, because only he knows where the obstacles are. I'm sang-froid. I'm going with the flow. Crap. I'm on red alert. I'm judging the milliseconds in portions of give and take, one step behind him. Too eager and I'll be a complete trollop, not keen enough will wipe me, without a trace, from the history of his back catalogue. Actually, I'm relying on theory because my lust is refusing to kick in. My hand shifts across his bum, and it's a different sort of bum, without the full content, as if compressed by decades of scholarly sitting. And I mustn't think of this, so I move my hand to the small of his back, less volatile, but not a lot, spongy. We've reached a leather sofa. I feel a pattern of upholstery dots at an arm end. He lays me gently down, as mature men do, and leans away to turn on a light, low, and the room jumps into life, sedately and opulently, discreetly, richly. There's a big painting above the sofa, and it's the real thing, I know this.

'That drink,' he says.

He smiles. It's ravishing, craggy.

'Lovely,' I say, and I pull my jumper into line.

'You're a very beautiful young woman,' he says.

It's not something that's likely to fail, is it? I'd like it in writing, though I know I'll never forget it, not even when I'm forty, I bet. And I make a note to tell my father this, the comment, because he so admires this man, this intellectual god, this Zeus, though naturally not what went before, or goes after – unless it's cerebral only.

And I wonder if he *needs* another drink, Dutch courage, surely not, or whether it's drink by rote and habit, for punctuation and pacing, simply to follow through. I need another drink, absolutely. I need one to fuse the sockets, cut the circuits, and obliterate the moral high ground. I need one to disable the alarms. He's looking at me the whole time, even as he knocks the ice cubes into tumblers and pours. And he strolls back across the room, and the glasses are clinking, and his roomy dark grey flannels are, nonetheless, straining at the crotch, which I'll take as a compliment because it's the sanest route. He is no beauty, in the conventional sense, and it's tricky. I'm trying hard to extricate his fame to see what's left, but he's all of a solid piece, with huge magnetic charm, and here I am, the iron filings. He hands me the glass, I take a gulp, he has a swig of his own and lays his glass down, on a marble tabletop, beside a big stack of serious books, the kind I haven't got to yet. I'm scanning the spines, and he's looking at me, crikey, like I'm the Mona Lisa, on his very sofa, but in jeans with a rip in the knee. He bends to remove my boots, and it's such a gentle and gentlemanly gesture but hopeless, because my laces are quadruple knotted to keep them out of the slush. Even so, they'll be sopping wet and impossible to budge without a struggle: anticipation and foresight, no, I hadn't any, for this fluke opportunity, this once in a lifetime chance, maybe, to be more than a footnote. And we might be here all night with these knots, because his close-to specs are out of reach. He looks up, he smiles, he shrugs, he gives up, he reaches out. And we are on the move again, the two of us plus the glass in my hand with the ice cubes knocking, and as he turns to open another door, I swallow the entire contents. The ice cubes slip down square in the through-routes of my chest.

It's all a bit Manet and *déjeuner sur l'herbe,* here on the counterpane; I am naked but for the boots, and he is fully clothed. And I'm thinking that it was a wise move, that he might have more authority with his clothes on than off, costly and well cut, which is not the situation with me. And he has his finger, ungloved now, naturally, or it would be extremely weird, at the top of my forehead and is running it slowly, slowly down in a line as if splitting me into two equal parts, down the centre of my nose and over my lips and chin, down my neck, and off across the hinterland of my body, his eyes peeled as he goes. It's not cold in here, with the steam heat wheezing, but I have goose pimples.

And now his finger is departing the dip of my navel and heading on south.

'Sorry,' I say.

'Mm?' he says.

'Loo,' I say.

'Sure,' he says, 'it's second left.' And he draws a line across my skin with his finger to mark the spot, and looks into my eyes, and smiles. 'I'll be waiting,' he says.

I slip off the bed and tap across the floor in my boots, past my clothes peeled off so beautifully by him, and dropped as we went, a little trail, the route map. I glance back and he blows a kiss, both subtle and generous. If all else fades, this one gesture will stick, I can tell. And he rolls onto his back to wait, with his hands cupped behind his head, his elbows out in Vs, his eyes fixed on me; odalisque, rear view.

At the front door I pull on my old damp coat. It weighs a ton. The ripped lining scuffs against my bare skin. And I wrap the coat round and hold it close, and let myself out, not a sound. I'll deal with the buttons in the lift.

II

We're entering through a side door, from a shifting heat to a static heat, when I see it.

'I'm pretty desperate,' I say.

'Don't be long,' he says.

'I'll see you up there,' I say.

'You'll love him,' he says, 'only, please, not too much.'

He laughs, and sandwiches my cheeks between his palms, not my best look. And off he goes, taking the stairs by twos, into the noise of people.

I'm not desperate, in that sense. I just need a pause, a moment's collection, to be able to slip into the talk after the chitchat of the foyer, the fandango of introductions, once the speaker is off in the wings. I spotted the invite in the apartment, and thought, any surprise but this. But here I am, the *bring a guest,* on my 28th birthday, before a late dinner in town.

I glance at my watch; eight minutes to go. And I swing into the restroom, and the door slaps shut behind me.

It's boiling hot and airless here, a bunker, without windows, snot green. It smells of summer drains. There are two strip lights, and one is flicking on and off, and buzzing. Four cubicles face four sinks and four mirrors. It's the end of the line for restoration, evidently, down in the bowels, with no air con, in August.

I run tepid water across my wrists, and check my face. I smile buoyantly. I see a mad person. I have a go at suave and cool. I walk to the door. And pull.

The knob comes off in my hand.

I push the knob back on, but the spindle and the outside knob thump to the floor out in the hall. I'm left holding the inside knob, adrift. I stick my finger into the hole that's left, and there's just emptiness. I push and pull at the door, rattle it, and kick it. I put my ear to it and shift and nudge, and listen, like you might when you're cracking a safe. Nothing. I lean back against the wall, sweating buckets, in my best dress.

I hear the rumble of applause from the floor above.

The trouble is, I like this man. I like him a lot, enough to be marrying him at City Hall next Tuesday so that I'm not deported when my visa runs out. I like him enough for a move to a white clapboard house in college town suburbia, a picket fence even, death maybe, though he's only renting, without tenure. And now my seat is sitting up there empty beside him, in that full auditorium. He'll think I've had cold feet. He'll think that I've slipped out to join the low life, not my style at all; *illegal alien* is such an unfriendly term. I don't even go without guilt through *Nothing to Declare* when I've nothing to declare. But he doesn't know this yet. He doesn't know that I wear small men's flannel pyjamas in winter, or like to read in the toilet. He doesn't know that I've met this speaker before. He'll blame himself for my no-show, on the visit to his former wife, on my birthday, although I said it was fine, that getting struck by a hit-and-run on a *walk* sign was simply her terrible bad luck, could happen to anyone, and we should have some empathy here. And, really, the children were very nice, even as they looked at me sideways. But my Black-Eyed Susans were practically dead in the heat. I should've gone for a better bunch, the ones with life support attached to each stem. I didn't want to overdo it though, this, my first *wife*. And she was lovely, despite the hospital gown and plaster leg. Actually, it was a relief to meet her incapacitated.

It's a relief too to have this birthday dress, low-key, designer, from the *once worn only by famous people* shop. I feel nearly unrecognizable. That seemed hopeful, for coming on here. It might not matter now, though. It might not matter either that there's sweat around my eye sockets, sliding down between my shoulder blades, gathering in the lines of my knicker elastic, pooling behind my knees. Or that strands of hair are clotted to my forehead. I'd take a drink from a tap, but the water might not be technically drinkable, in a public restroom, in Manhattan. *Foreigner in Squalid City John Water Shock Fatality*. I skipped those bits of the guidebook, the *handy typhoid tips,* maybe, *the bubonic plague and you.* Art & Culture, what use now?

I feel the vibration of the city through my Dr Martens, through their buffered soles, their red-hot insides, right up into the whole of me. I bet the toilet bowl water is trembling with the tumult of it all. But I'm staying here, up against the wall, saving my energy. The air has the weight of syrup. I can't find the oxygen in it, not in any recognizable form. There must be the proper sort upstairs, with coolness pumped in, to leave room for laughter, I can hear it; amused, informed, enlightened. It's all very droll, I'm pretty sure. And if no one nips out in all that number, if no one responds to the smallest urinary infection or a touch of food poisoning, it's because this talk's compulsive, magnetic. I feel it right through the concrete, even.

Anyway, the First World facilities are on the First World floor.

I'm shut in for the duration. It's mortifying. It's a stroke of luck.

I rummage in my bag, bring out a book, and flap it in front of my face. The molecules nudge and bump, turgid. It's a book for moments like this, the subway and other shut-in places, to be instantly out of body, treading in other people's missteps and screw-ups, their wrong choices, their hatchet jobs through the privilege of large houses with sprawling lawns, automated sprinklers and hired help, in some east coat paradise. There's no limit to the quantity of wrong choices made, devastation caused, chances of salvation missed, guilt to be dealt with, and boredom tholed. And just when you think it can get no worse, it does. It's quite a comfort.

*

There's applause, extended and lavish. Doors fly open, people are on the move. Little spikes of laughter shoot up above the babble. A whole auditorium empties out into the hot night, through the correct doors on the floor above, the ones that do not land you here, in purgatory. Then there is silence.

And I'm leaning hotly on a sink, and flipping a page, and our hero is rashly telling the whole truth and all hell is breaking loose, when I hear feet on the stairs, two pairs.

'Hello?' he says.

'I'm stuck,' I say.

He rattles the door. 'It's stuck,' he says.

'I know,' I say.

He is slotting the handle in on the other side. I'm trying to recollect *suave,* but what I've got, when I glance in the mirror, is *sedated.* He opens the door.

And there they both are, of course, standing in a little posse of cool: the man I will marry on Tuesday and his colleague, the speaker, Zeus. Zeus languishes nonchalant against the corridor wall, tanned, in a dark grey linen suit, tie loosened at the neck, a sprig of grizzled chest hair escaping; six years on, you wouldn't know it. He smiles, it's ravishing. I feel weak at the knees, with fear. He reaches out a hand, courteous, flattering, compelling, wise, witty, absolutely *on,* eyes flicking to my near-nil cleavage slick with perspiration; delighted to meet me, this friend of his friend. And there's not the smallest double take. No narrowing of the eyes, no delay, hesitation, or *haven't we met before?* Nothing. Not a thing. I am wiped from the record, erased and expunged. The panic was pointless, the stress surplus, the bathroom a useless detour – the relief is epic, and the truth quite awful if you dwell on it, being so forgettable.

And he takes my hand and squeezes it warmly, without a trace of hidden message or private meaning.

'Not many go to such lengths,' he says, 'to avoid my talks.'

And we all laugh, there in the bathroom. And my laugh's a little too loud – not sedated at all but on the edge of hysterics, and I'd love a rewind button, to be able to start again, to pick another sort; laconic, mature, unfazed, no big deal, about being entombed, about this Zeus standing right here in *my* toilet – which would be the worst nightmare, if he hadn't wiped one night clear off his radar. And he leans in to kiss my cheek, generously and seductively, in no way senior-citizenly. And I feel his stubble on the side of my face, and his breath on my neck. I feel his lips against my ear. I hear his voice, deep-throated and rich and just for me.

'Nice boots,' he says.

III

'Wow, cool shoes,' she says.

'Aren't they,' I say.

'New?' she says.

I lay down the newspaper to take a better look. I raise my feet. I rotate my ankles.

'Not particularly,' I say, 'but hardly worn. They're impossible to walk in.'

I look at my watch. I flick a bit of dust off my little black dress.

'Confidence, that's all,' she says. 'I'll just say hello to Fred.'

She strides off through the French windows in her cut-offs and bare feet, out across the lawn, her shadow ten feet long in the late sun, ripping navy-blue through the foliage and beds. Her unwavering confidence is a pain in the neck. But you can only ask an A-student to baby-sit; a B-student might take revenge and reveal what you have around the house, in the drawers even, like the new class lists with scribbled erasable prompts: *teeth* next to Jane, *spots* next to Jim. Or the pills for panic in the bathroom cabinet.

And now she's closing in on Fred. He's kneeling out there at the edge of the lawn, digging holes in the herbaceous border, consolidating worms into one deep pit. He says it's for research. He says he'll let me know if they set up a commune, or become cannibals, or whatever. *Worm eat worm,* he said this morning, and he fell about in fits of mirth, the six-year-old sort, and landed in a bed of phlox. Flattened phlox seemed the least of it today. And the stripes on his t-shirt were sore to the eyes.

Fred looks up and squints towards the sun, and he sees the babysitter, unmistakable even in silhouette, curls all haloed in gold. And he jumps up, and hops about, and hunkers back down, and shoves a loop of mousy hair behind his ear. And he's gesticulating and talking fast, non-stop. He leans into the hole, half disappeared, and brings out a worm, his prize worm probably, because I see it from here, huge and slimy and wriggling. And he hands it to her, like a token of love, maybe, and she takes it, unflinching, attentive, because who knows, in twenty years Fred might be someone.

♦

18

And I'm thinking it's good that she's not in my husband's subject area, but mine, though not foolproof, because collaboration between departments scores points in this hothouse of excellence, the non-physical kind. *Touch* a student and you're done for, even in empathy, even if their whole family's just been wiped out. A lawyer was brought in at the start of the year to tell us all this. We sat in rows, boggle-eyed, with litigation.

And I look at my pointy feet, and at the room here, and the rosy glow of sunset saturating everything except the neon wedge of lime in my g & t suspended among the ice cubes. I stroke the sofa. I smooth the newspaper, the page I'm at. I'd stay here all evening if I could, facing the lawn and the lengthening shadows, with alternate legs crossed, rotating my ankles. But tonight's party is for me. I wish it wasn't. I wish my cool would get a move on. I'm hoping that the muscles for chutzpah and risk haven't atrophied out here in paradise, that I haven't forgotten the old thrills of the city – of blowing my nose and finding nothing but filth, of grit lining my coat pocket seams, and the light-bulbs all blazing bright in the outré bits of the head where chance, danger and proper remorse hang out. Today seemed a good day to prove that it's not all just the ghost of a thing, like a kiss blown, maybe, like dog-shit somewhere about the place, on someone's foot, wafting. So this morning I rolled up my jeans and put on these shoes, and took a coffee outside, to practise. And my eyes skimmed the top of the hedge there, six feet tall, and across it there was nothing but rippling barley, right to the horizon. And I tapped and wobbled back and forth on the path, in air that hadn't got boiling hot yet, and after a bit Fred looked up from his worms, anxious.

'It's – all right,' I called, 'I'm – forty – today.'

And he mouthed *oh, yeah,* and got back to digging.

He's got used to half-worms, the collateral damage.

And now the babysitter is dropping the worm back in the hole. *Safekeeping,* she'll be saying. I see her wipe her palm on her hip, the one that's not facing Fred, and she turns and strolls back across the lawn. I'm the only audience, from the front, anyway, but her stroll is choreographed, as if some luminary, some influential potentate or notable guest-lecturer-type is lounging about among the hollyhocks, which they do sometimes, having a smoke.

And now she steps inside.

'Any luck,' she says, 'with the shoes?'

'I haven't moved an inch,' I say.

'It's just *attitude*, honestly,' she says.

'I've mislaid *attitude*,' I say. 'Here, you have a go.'

And I lean over and pull the strappy things from my feet. My toes stay squashed together, in fright, maybe. And she slips the shoes on, and sets off, and moves about the room to show me how, and she's right, it *is* attitude, and I don't have it. And she settles on the sofa arm, crosses her legs, and angles a foot like in the mags, although the muscles to keep it there must be strained rigid. She tilts her head sideways, and looks down at the newspaper. And there is Zeus, smiling back – ravishing, amused, at some little joke long gone to dust, his crowded teeth brilliant white, his hair dark and flipped by a wind, his pale cuffs rolled and top button slipped, a sea glittering beyond, and half a vertical woman in a patterned shift–dress and slender arm pressed to his shirt sleeve, nineteen sixty-seven. *Dead at Eighty* is written in bold.

'Ever meet him?' she asks. 'Conferences, whatever?'

'Once or twice,' I say.

'Wow, you actually *knew* him!' she says.

'Well, not biblically,' I say.

I laugh. She laughs, a bark, a whoop. 'If only!' she says.

I fold away the paper, and say I must be off, and if she can get Fred out of the worms pretty soon that'll be great. And through the French windows the sprinkler sends its first arc of spray across the lawn, on the timer, on the dot, although really the grass is green enough.

'You keep the shoes,' I say. 'They'll never work for me.'

KERRY HOOD

TXL

It is Tuesday and Christmas is over but the coming of a bigger thing is three sleeps away and is called The Millennium. Every day the clear part of my head wakes me up then pings off and leaves the room as though it was a just a joke. On Tuesdays I go to the Dorset South Centre For Community Learning where you can learn to love Jesus or line-dancing. The Centre is opposite my flat. Next to it is the Dorset South School of Dancing. When I'm sitting in the Centre, I can hear the dancing and the tape recorder, or the piano if it is a ballet examination. I never go in because of my eight-year-old injury, which means I do appropriate activities for my particular circumstances. My local community pays for me to stay out of dancing schools and the local community.

You can do something every day at the Centre and have your Monday to Sunday timetabled away and never need to make up your life from scratch. I could go every day but I have my own timetable, which fills up the front part of my head and barricades it against the clearer dangerous part. People with special needs go to the Centre. They have an inability to see or hear or talk or walk or all of those connecting things. Normal people go. They have an inability to stencil chairs or go up and down a step to music. They watch the special needs people and say there but for the grace of God go I fancy being deaf dumb blind limpy how awful bless I'd shoot myself. They say it with their backs to the notice board that says British Sign Language Course Cancelled Due To Lack Of Signatures.

I have lived in this road for three years, from when I was no longer called an orphan but an adult, no longer in need of the Home, though I still didn't have any parents. This September Stefan wrote to the Dorset South Centre For Community Learning. He works at the Home and was assigned to particular orphans and other unwanted people. My address must have been filed in the wrong filing drawers because Stefan didn't know where I was for three years. He must have wanted to make up for it with a surprise because I had no idea I was on a course until the letter came with the date and the room number.

The letter told me to go to the Centre for ten o'clock in the morning, which is late for me because I like to go out when no one is around. The letter said to go with essential equipment to Room 1IT where I would be allocated a course appropriate to my level. So I took my purse with my door key in the pocket of my long coat, which is essential to wrap around my legs, which are fat because of the drugs. I'm not angry at the drugs. They are only trying to stop your hips hurting. They have to get into them, which they do, but it makes you keep your coat on.

The Centre is really an old church hall. I found Room 1IT and waited for my surprise. On one of the desks was a course name. Stupid was part of it. Computing For The Stupid. I left the room.

I was hot and breathing too much. I couldn't remember whether I had to go along the corridor to get out or turn back. I must have been Stupid. I decided to have a think because my walk attracts attention and the corridor was filling up. I looked into Room 1CFTT while my head slowed. Suddenly, someone put their hand on my shoulder, behind me, on the collar of my coat, touching my hair. My father used to come up behind me and the last time he did it, he tried to murder me. I screamed – inside – outside Room 1CFTT and held my breath, until a clear part said my father was dead, and I let it out and it sweat over the glass door.

Two hands were on my shoulders, turning my body to look at a man. I am five feet and half an inch. This man wasn't much taller and he had no hair except for white-grey sticks in a curve from behind one ear to the other, like a fringe on a sofa. He wore gold glasses on a red cord that might have been dipped in minestrone soup. It was hard to say how old he was but there were brown spots on his hands. They weren't spots of minestrone soup. They were spots that make you over half your life old, which was confusing because the man's eyes in his polished face made him look about eleven. He held open the door and said welcome welcome we shan't begin lift-off until ten thirty hours but I sense a kindred early-bird spirit welcome my dear step upon the launch pad of discovery!

He said it with an exclamation mark as though he was full of an eleven year-old's beans and I knew I shouldn't think about making a decision. I shouldn't think. I said thank you. I went in.

Room 1CFTT was a set of long grey desks, from one wall to the next until they reached the centre. Opposite each chair was a computer, keyboard and other connecting things which I couldn't call anything then.

The man pulled out a spinning chair and I sat down. He didn't put his hands on my shoulders because I think he knew not to. He took off his jacket. I was glad for him. It looked itchy. He started whistling, took paper and pencils from an old brown briefcase and put one of each next to the screens. I looked at my sheet of paper. There was typing on one side, a page five of something. The man said scrap my dear waste not want not would you be happier with the window open may I take your coat it is a temperate September.

I said thank you. The man nodded. All the same, I held my coat around me. Three people came into the room all saying something together like a sneeze. Hello. They turned to me and said it. Hello. The man said welcome welcome. I looked down at my paper. Someone came in and gave him a list. He sighed and said only three this year seller-vee seller-vee.

Then he came to us with a sticker for our names, which we had to wear. He said the powers do love their badges so we shall kow-tow to them for today. His badge didn't have a name. It was a brassy badge of a flying saucer. When he put my sticker on the desk he looked at his list, then said my dear your name isn't here but thank heavens you are, three is a tragedy whereas four is a delight.

To all of us, he said I'm Head Whitey Kay but call me Captain as I shall be steering us through galaxies where we shall make mincemeat of technical minefields, where we shall discover universes at the depression of a digit, where we shall conquer phobia with fun and flexible fingering.

Everyone laughed. Then he said welcome to Computing For The Terrified. I looked down and into my coat. He said hands up honestly hands up you're among friends, hands up who is terrified?

The others put their hands up, and then Captain did the same and everyone laughed. I put mine up. He said never forget it is only artificial intelligence we are its masters and mistresses so I want you good people to strap yourselves in and prepare for take off.

He told us everything, from the beginning. He waited for us to do what he said, always behind us, but not pressing down on our heads. He showed us how to switch on our computers and said we have contact. He made us say it, together. We have contact. I mimed. We typed our names and thought of a password. It had to be letters and numbers and you couldn't tell anyone else. I found that part easy. Then we were given a CD – they were supposed to cost one pound fifty but Captain said what is one pound fifty between friends – which was to be ours alone, and suddenly I had a part-feeling I was to stay separate, with my own disk and secret code, and

I didn't feel grateful. Although it wasn't the first time I had thought it, that Tuesday three months ago was the first time I said inside, please bring me into the world. Show me the world, with me in it.

Yet, sitting nearest the window I knew that a keeping-apart disk was essential for keeping alive, for avoiding being misunderstood and half-killed and orphaned. When I walk, even now, my father re-half-kills me and it hurts.

Captain was saying beam us up Scotty, all press enter, wait for it wait for it…all crew press Enter – now!

I jumped back in my chair as the world came alive in colour and sound. I looked at the other computers, all with the same colours, sounds. We were all in it. We saw icons and programs, and documents without staples and folders without folds and files without drawers, one connecting to another one, one kept inside one until you asked for it. It wasn't easy. You had to concentrate. You had to match the arrow on the screen with your hand. After we had pointed and clicked to learn a particular thing, Captain said do have a play, it won't bite, enjoy it, that's an order crew!

The four of us were slow to play. We could see each other with our side-eyes not wanting to make a wrong beep. Then one of us coughed and said here goes oh what happened there Captain I've cocked it up already trust me to be the first one what does You Cannot Delete This File mean?

Then the other two started moving their mouse and clicking, then frowning and not quite believing it, as though a glass was spelling out where their grandma had buried her jewellery. Captain was helping to uncock and undelete and saying well done you, that didn't hurt did it, heads up crew.

He stood behind the chairs, going from the woman who had cocked it up to a man who wanted to know how long it would take to get his certificate, to another man in a blue jacket with a sewn-on badge, who called Captain chief and said it was all Greek. I quickly looked at my screen because Captain was coming over. My hand was on top of the mouse, all dead. It wasn't my good hand. He was behind my chair and I was working out how I could hide the burned hand and I stopped breathing in.

He leaned over and looked at my screen, then at my hand. Before I had time to pull my sleeve over it, Captain Whitey Kay covered it, on the mouse, with his own hand. He moved it to the left and pressed just enough to make my finger click and change the screen, then to the right to unchange it and again two, three, twenty times, until my shoulders went down and I breathed out, until I saw I had changed something myself. Good my dear. I said thank you. I felt his tie tickle my ear. He patted my burned hand and said good my dear well done.

For a person with artificial intelligence, he was the most real since my homeless temporary friend Munshy. At one o'clock a buzzer went off and Captain said please be back at two on the dot, feel free to risk the canteen. Everyone laughed and again because the man in the blue blazer said I can't remember the last time I went to a canteen chief it takes me back to cabbage.

Captain had to lock the windows and door and told us he would catch us up. The others laughed shakily along the corridor, all echoey, and I followed behind as quickly as my hips would let me without looking too much like the timer on top of a piano. At a double door we had to turn left and face another one. When the lady who'd cocked it up opened the door, ten rows of tables and heads were facing us. The young man who'd asked about a certificate went next, then the man with the blue blazer. I couldn't catch the door. It swung at me. The others were walking towards the food cabinets, beyond the glass, and I went home.

I didn't go back at two o'clock. For the rest of the week, I felt half-done. Every time I looked at my hand, I thought of the mouse and where it almost took me. I wanted to feel safe more than I wanted to join the world. Yet I also knew it had been the best chance to have a Tuesday timetable for one whole term.

So the next Tuesday I sat in Room 1CFTT. I don't think Captain noticed I hadn't come back from lunch the week before. He said welcome Miss Early-Bird would you be a trooper and set out the paper and wake up the computers and open the window you are a godsend my dear.

I did what he asked, all the time thinking what I might need help with, what my special needs were, how Captain might lean over and tickle my ear with his tie. I would try not to jump this time. I sat by the window but Captain asked me to turn off that monitor as it had crashed and to use the one nearest the others. They arrived, we pressed Enter and the world opened up and I didn't think about Captain and his tie because he was behind all of us and that was enough until one o'clock.

They went left and I went the other way to go home, until Captain called that I must have forgotten the way. The man who'd asked about the certificate said come on babe the food is pants but the coffee I'm telling you it's the best it's well good.

I was scared in the canteen. The others bought food – I had a tuna sandwich already made at home but I daren't go back now – while I sat and looked at their badges. The lady who'd cocked it up was Mrs. Blanche Al-something. Her badge wasn't long enough. She had shaky hands and laughed high up with her mouth shut. She had black hair like a teardrop and grey eyebrows. She used to be a secretary in the Seventies and wanted to learn computing because her husband had gone.

Marc was the young one who thought the food was like pants. His hair reached his trousers and was in the tubes of a black person and he was white. You couldn't know, definitely, what he was. That was brave of him, to do it on purpose. He knew about computers but had to get a certificate to prove he wasn't terrified. He didn't have a job, he said, because he saw words backwards and letters all over the place. The man in the blue blazer had been in North Africa in the war but his great-grandchildren thought his stories were boring compared to computer war games, so he was learning to fight another battle. He had entirely white hair and a beard with red in it, or ketchup, and he was called Potter, W.G. Then there was me. The only four Terrified people in our seaside town.

Mrs. Blanche Al-something told us she liked the course apart from the fact she didn't understand anything and that Captain called her Mrs. Almond, like blanched almonds but that he probably didn't get out much because of having a dead wife. Potter, W.G. pointed out that Captain Whitey Kay was wasting time with his rubbish about lift-off. He said it's *them* you want to worry about, storing our information so they can get rid of the defectives and OAPs – these computers are Hitlers in a box – but I'll be ready when they switch over to two zero zero zero oh yes.

Marc asked how will you be ready? Gonna make your cyber self invisible? Cos that's like impossible cos the government and the military are like this massive hard drive whale – when we click, it opens its gob and in we pour like little fishes.

Potter, W.G. stared at him, patted his stomach and said I'll tell you something lad, I would swap the present Mrs. Potter for another of these egg custards. He went to the counter. Marc said Captain is well cool he's off his head. I nodded, not because I agreed, but because Marc had bought me a coffee, which I wouldn't have accepted, but the others were looking and I had to get them to stop. Marc said it's real coffee not freeze-dried pants. I drank the coffee. It was the best I had ever tasted. After lunch, Mrs. Blanche Al-something cocked it up and laughed and Captain called her Mrs. Blanched Almond and she laughed louder.

Every Tuesday I have set out the paper and woken up the computers and sat near the others. Now we have our certificates to confirm we are not Terrified. A new course starts next month if computers allow us to go into another century. We didn't learn how to use the Internet because there is a policy of not exposing beginners to cyber felons. I don't know what that means. The next course is how to edit a newsletter and design your own flat-house with all of its rooms. It is 2CFTLS, Computing For the Less Scared. I can't go, because the Crash is coming.

*

This morning I looked out of my window to the Centre, which is on its Christmas holidays. I thought about the connecting things I never used to know the names of. I missed talking without talking, seeing without being seen. A light was on in one of the rooms. It looked like 2CFTLS. I went out of the side door with its Special garden and looked left and right. The road was empty. The Minnellium Big Crash Sales were on. People were choosing to spend their last moments on the twentieth century earth in Debenhams. This gave me a push of courage. I went over to Room 2CFTLS. Captain Whitey Kay was at a computer.

Welcome welcome my dear.

He guided me into a chair. He had dark rings of sad dreams under his eyes. I sat down and Captain stood behind. I felt the tickle of the scarf. The computer was asking me where I wanted to go and what was my screen name. I started to get hot. It was waiting for an answer. I might get stuck somewhere. I might get abandoned in space. In my flat, in most of my head, in the library and other places in my timetable, I was alone and I suddenly realised that here in computer space it should be no different. Captain typed his name – it wasn't Whitey Kay – and a password of stars. He told me to click Connect then he opened a packet of mince pies, saluted and said you have your pilot's licence my dear, your first solo mission to cyberspace.

I was into a Public Chat Room. You watch other people talking, one line each. Everyone can see and pretend-hear everyone else. You add a line. If it is a voice you don't want to listen to, you can click it out. FourEx and SiberMensch and Geekydick were talking in misspellings called abbreviations. Lines of red and blue and grey were falling down the page like fish from a giant net and disappearing before you had time to hook them. I couldn't catch anything in my Net. I put my hand on the mouse to leave the room and saw the screen name samMD with the message

Where Are You Tuesday World? WAY, Tuesday World?

No one answered. The line came again, but other lines followed, such as

What Happened In Xmas special Corrie?
TXL For Last Nite FanC Meet L8R?
Some1 croaked
Ubet CYA

and dots and dashes that looked like sideways humans. You couldn't delete any of it and it wouldn't be nice. I thought here I am, without showing my fat red face, looking at the Tuesday world without using that hot part, without having to call up the voice scared into hiding. I typed

Here I Am, HIA, Tuesday World. I'm nearly in it. Are you?

It appeared, my screen voice – CaptainY2K. I felt as though I'd thrown a stone at a speeding car and had no wall to crouch behind. I closed my eyes. I opened them. A message came falling down the screen.

samMD: Leave the room CaptainY2K. Meet in mine 1-2-1.

I had asked a question, in a pretend voice, and had received an answer. I looked at Captain. He nodded, showed me how to get into a Private Room, took a penknife, halved a mince pie and put it near me. He looked over my shoulder the entire time but it felt like it was just me. I typed in the abbreviation for the only word I ever spoke out loud in the real world – TXL – and left the public part.

samMD lived in My Favourite Places in space but wrote that he also lived in my town and that it was Kismet. Maybe it was one of the new estates.

My Favourite Places was my favourite place. I had no hip-hurting walk or fat red face or lips moving with no sound coming out. We used no more abbreviations, apart from UC, which meant we both saw. Understood Completely. In all other conversation we used whole words. We built them up. samMD spoke without symbols. He told me about growing up in our town. When he wrote about the sea, the words blew warm and salty across the screen. He told me about sailing with his brother, about waves that slapped you full in the face, about keeping your head down in case the sail knocked you out. He put words in an order that made you laugh. You would have laughed out loud. I wanted to but didn't know if cyberspace was as far up as heaven and whether my father could hear.

samMD typed really slowly as though his keyboard was thinking about the shapes it was making. He never paid his own Internet bills. The local authority did. He typed that we had been given the gift of communication and that it was a cliché but true. He didn't ask me to make a picture of my life, about my growing up in the same town. I told him I had a sister and a mother and that I used to live in Cyprus. Captain looked at me and was probably calling me a liar, inside. I should have pressed Escape but it seemed that until then everyone had been talking Vietnamese and that suddenly, after staring at foreign mouths, I realised I understood and could talk in the same language with the same connecting things.

samMD was typing slower. He asked me to understand that I was creating an electronic life and that he was living it with me. He said understand that when you let a thing out you give it a meaning forever. You can let the person reading your life decide what it means. You can Cut and Paste the order, but the meaning is there, in between what you don't write. He wrote

Your life has meaning you are validated not invalid.

I read his line and straightaway typed

Not an invalid no. Are you?

HAHA. Seeing as you ask, yes. Yes I am.

*

I went home. Even though it is only opposite the Centre, by the time I had walked around the chair to stop my hips hurting, I was breathing as though my ribs were poking my lungs. I didn't want to think. I sent it straight to the part of my head that works like a machine for cutting paper into strips. Only, the words started to stick themselves back together, to remind me that invalid means disabled and disabled means lying on your back with your dead mother on top of you.

samMD was a symbol. He had spoken in symbols after all. He had used artificial intelligence to tell lies. I wanted a normal friend. I had believed our electronic life was exploding like an exciting experiment, that it was bringing me into the real world without making me speak or be seen, that I was learning the language of the real world, anonymous, familiar. I had been a pretend normal person.

Now I knew I was also a liar. I had not built a word-picture of my hip-hurting walk or my fat drug-made face. My father had heard me write that silence. He was punishing me from cyberspace heaven, so that now, out of all the billions of cyber people, I was kept in my town with someone wearing an own-label like mine. It didn't make me a nice person to say it, even though I was only saying inside.

I left Captain with his mince pies. I've still got my coat on. I'm looking at the Centre from my windows. It is not a new building, but it is not historic enough to have an 'e' at the end of old to make it somewhere American people would visit. Princess Diana came once. It was a secret. She was wearing trousers. It was in the newspapers. She was laughing in the photograph, a dangerously big laugh. She wasn't saying anything, just laughing, but you could see she was saying something. You could see the faces of the people in a half-circle, nearly touching her. It was like someone taking a picture of an unidentified flying object and developing the film, and the object isn't there. It is there, in its itness.

Munshy was someone else I nearly knew. He disappeared yesterday – at least, I discovered it yesterday. He lived in a home where homeless people live. Now he must be a former homeless home person who may be entirely homeless. I cannot think about it. It is confusing and finished. It was Monday.

Captain is across the road, tightening his scarf. I hope he's got a vest on. He looks over. I don't want him in my Special flat-house. He might look around my white walls and at my stacks of tuna and say how awful bless I'd shoot myself.

Only, I feel guilty leaving a man with a dead wife and possibly no vest three days after Christmas. Ten minutes later I get into his car, trying not to think. On the way to samMD's Home, Captain says my dear these things happen, you are a friend indeed, this chap is called Sam and is a friend in need, he can no longer write happily, look in the box at your feet, I have a little invention for this very situation.

In the box is a soft helmet with a headband across the top and padding down each cheek like sideburns and a spongy pocket like a bra cup to go under the chin. The bra cup is an invented mouse. The sideburns are invented arrows. You move your cheeks and an arrow points at a keyboard on the computer screen. The headband is an Enter key. You frown and you are back in the world. Captain must know samMD.

I am scared. We are at the Dorset South Muscular Dystrophy Home, in a computer room. Captain presses my shoulder forward to a wheelchair and the back of a big man wearing a leather jacket with silver bolts in the shape of an eagle. I can smell the leather because Sam has written about this jacket. He doesn't turn. His hands bend over the wheelchair tyres. I stop breathing in. I am behind him. I put the soft helmet on his head and he doesn't move. He must be angry which is understandable. Perhaps he would try to kill me if his hands worked. I have leaned over with Captain's helmet, like a crown, and I say –inside – everything about how I feel. How I feel never comes out and today is no different, except that today I want it to come, with my entire self.

I straighten up and look back at Captain who goes towards the door. I go to follow him and suddenly a bent hand slides across my arm. I put my burned hand over Sam's bent hand. Without thinking, just doing. My lips don't move, yet it is like clicking Send.

Captain drives me back to Room 2CFTLS and we wait in the Private Chat Room. My eyes close, trying to feel into my head my own voice, trying to remember its outside sound, its password. It seems we wait for a century, until Captain says my dear look my dear look.

I open my eyes as cyberspace fog clears on the screen and I see
T...X...L...T...X...L
and I type back
T...X...L
but my inside voice adds
you're welcome, my friend.

SHEILA CRAWFORD

Oyster Woman

Esther can hear the sea above the gale. Windows and doors rattle; the chimney screams; the dogs lie, ears back, flat against her sides, whining their anxiousness at her face in puffs of crabby breath – they'd both been at the bins yesterday evening. She waits in the half dark for the song in her head to take shape. She won't be able to sleep until she knows how the whole will sound. It doesn't have to be perfect, just good enough to write out before breakfast, before giving Lark and Spur a run in the dunes. Meanwhile, the waves smash at the walls of the fort.

Let the stones crumble. Crack eggs in the nests.

Esther checks the time on her mobile. In twenty-five minutes, her neighbour will begin shifting his boat into the street from his garage. Every day, he goes through the same manoeuvres. He moves his car a few metres up the hill. He rolls up the garage doors. He heaves the boat across the road on its trailer. He swings it back towards the waiting car, locks it in tow position and then reverses the assembled unit to block the entrance to his garage. His name is Paul Meunier, according to the label on the mailbox.

'Do you fish?' Esther said the first morning. 'I'm Esther, Esther Mannington. I've bought *La Chamade*. Next door.'

He shook her outstretched hand.

'Why do you ask?'

Esther pointed at the boat.

'No. And I don't take groups of tourists round the bay. I indulge myself. You have dogs. I have a boat.'

Paul and Esther rarely talk. Of course, they exchange greetings. Unavoidable in a small village. They don't chat; they don't pass on information. It wasn't from Paul that Esther learned the history of her house.

It began life as an apartment above a butcher's shop. The butcher jumped in the sea from the fort's rampart because his wife ran away with the pharmacist's teenage son. The hairdresser, who took over the business part of the building, left the upper floors to damp and fungal infestations. When he couldn't ignore any longer the general decay, he swung the notice on the door to 'closed' and left the keys at the nearest estate agency with instructions to sell at any price. For a while, the agent used the ground floor as a subsidiary office, patched up the accommodation and let the rooms to holidaymakers looking for a cheap rental. The hairdresser found out, insisted on a sale. Esther, the English musician, turned up with two dogs and a French bank account.

'I want to die within sight and sound of the sea,' she said.

'You're too young, Madame,' said the agent.

'People die at any age,' said Esther.

'More of the old than the young.'

'Except in times of war.'

'Fortunately, we are not at war,' he said. 'Is there no Monsieur Mannington?'

'He was a soldier. He was killed.'

The agent expressed his regrets. 'I spoke thoughtlessly,' he said. 'We tend to forget Iraq and Afghanistan.'

Esther didn't explain that Robert had joined a cult, become a Soldier of Christ. The coach he was driving to Birmingham for an evangelical conference had crashed on the motorway in perfect weather conditions. The agent would spread the word in the village that she was a military widow. Fine. When she was thirteen, she used to dream of marrying a man in army uniform, not some hairy-jumpered religious nut.

Nobody, in the event, showed much interest in her arrival at Les Coulisses. The place has a proper name on maps and signposts, a web page. Locally, however, it calls itself Les Coulisses.

'Why?' Esther said to the ex-biker who runs the bar.

He shrugged. 'Why not? Lost in history.'

'Doesn't it confuse visitors?'

'What visitors? Visitors don't come any more. Since the accident.'

'Accident?'

He rustled the pages of his sporting paper.

'Ask your neighbour.'

Esther ordered another espresso. He either didn't hear or didn't want to. She left two euros on the metal table, untied the dogs from the railing and made her way home.

In spite of its air of vacancy, Les Coulisses doesn't depress Esther. It's a home. Most of the year, most of the buildings stand empty. Apart from the Bar des Sports, the only remaining commercial enterprise is a mini superette with parking for at least a hundred cars. In the summer months, a few market stalls appear every Friday morning.

Even in August, locals outnumber tourists. It's the kind of seaside resort where people leave their houses unlocked and wander down to the beach after work in their bathing gear, towel draped round their shoulders. They nod at Esther without curiosity. Esther doesn't swim; she can't swim. Her children used to tease her about it. 'That way, I'll never drown,' she told them.

The children are all coming. Soon. Maybe next Sunday. They're hiring a car. She'll have to ask Paul Meunier to give her extra space. One vehicle could, of course, be left round the corner in the cul-de-sac that ends where the dunes begin.

She throws on her father's old camel dressing gown, her comfort garment, and catches her neighbour as he finishes straightening and attaching the boat.

She makes her request.

He stares.

'It will be for ten days. Two weeks at the outside.'

'Your belt is very frayed. I have a spare one I can let you have.'

Esther glances down at the cord, tugs it more tightly round her waist. 'The dogs; they chew on it. They used to have rubber bones with tassels to play with. I lost them in the dunes.'

'Do your children like the dogs?'

'I don't know. Does it matter?'

'Probably not.'

'About the parking?'

'I'll allow you part of my section of the road,' he says.

Esther cannot tell whether he is odd or simply having fun at her expense.

'Have a good morning,' she says.

He doesn't respond.

Two hours later, Esther finds a plaited silk dressing gown cord coiled on her front step.

The children fall in love with Les Coulisses. Esther is discovering areas of the village she didn't know existed until the three of them burst into her life. Since they left home, and more or less stopped visiting her one at a time, she has to make an effort to name them as separate individuals. They are the children. Would you children take the dogs for a walk? Do you children want mussels for supper? Are you children warm enough? They all work in hot places of the world.

In her head, she has begun to refer to them as the Greek Chorus. Although they yelp their appreciation of Les Coulisses at every opportunity – its bay, its weird convict history, its shell strewn shoreline, its one long street plunging into the harbour at the end of the slipway, its surly inhabitants – they can't see any good coming from her settling in such a place.

'We don't think you're safe.'

'The bloke next door avoids us.'

'What if you broke a leg and couldn't drive?'

'The dunes could be full of old land mines.'

And when they hear about the accident, Esther locks herself in her room to drown out the doom chorus.

'I've a song cycle to finish for Maisie Croft. We'll talk later.'

Esther is peeved, not worried. In two days, the children have wormed out all the details concerning the accident that apparently ruined the village as a tourist destination. She ferreted away. Nobody told her a dickybird. They let her go on eating the molluscs.

'How many died?'

The children answered as one voice. 'Five adults, two children.'

'Seven is a significant number,' Esther said. It certainly is: reverse numbers on a dice always add up to seven.

Paul Meunier used to take groups, mostly Parisians, on gentle fishing excursions along the coast, not too far out, not in rough seas. At the end of an outing, he hosted an alfresco feast in the shelter of the dunes. He liked a fishy theme so his clients would leave with the impression of having tasted their catch. They rarely caught anything. Which was just as well. Gutting fish is a disappearing art.

The day of the accident, the children told her, Paul's picnic supper consisted of oysters he'd gathered himself from the old commercial beds at low tide. He'd forgotten about the wreck of the tanker, months ago in the winter. Sad sea birds, wings brilliantined to their bodies, flapping in sinks of detergent, had disappeared from TV screens.

In the event, nobody was sure the oyster contamination came from crude oil. An ancient storm drain sometimes flushed its contents on the beach, spewing tampons, nappies and sewage for gulls to pick over.

E.coli?

Seven deaths don't go away. Shifted into folklore from news item, they stay to taint collective memories.

Paul received no official condemnation. Misadventure is an adventure gone wrong. The human psyche, however, needs blame more urgently than forgiveness or redemption. Les Coulisses sent Paul to French Coventry, not in a fit of pique but as a permanent exclusion.

'Bunch of morons,' he said when they spat on his boat.

'You could write a song about him,' the children suggested.

'Since when has my work interested you children?'

'You didn't ever share it with us. You always shut yourself away.'

'Yes, I know.'

'With the infernal squeaking recorder.'

They used to ask her, when they noticed what she was doing, why she didn't compose at the piano.

'A keyboard's too orchestral.'

They harrumphed and rolled eyes.

Esther is lying in bed, running the new dressing gown cord through her fingers. Her neighbour has gone to Paris for a few days. The house is creaking, timbers moving in the emptiness. The children are somewhere in the dunes with Lark and Spur. They have no patience with her bout of food poisoning.

'You should know better. The dogs get the squits when they've been licking around those scummy rock pools. You eat stuff. Raw bits from shells,' they say when they return.

The Greek Chorus.

They bring her lemonade from the superette and a packet of factory-baked madeleines.

'Don't stand around my bed, looking like that. I feel I'm in a gloomy Spanish play.'

Shouts from the street draw them to the window. Voices, not shouts. They seem like shouts because the village is so silent. Les Coulisses could be one of those preserved destroyed places – a volcanic disaster, a plague hamlet, a site of war horror. We walk through them softly, showing respect, trying hard to think 'let those who are without sin cast the first stone' thoughts. But hating.

The whine of a metal saw drives Esther to join her children at the window.

Four men in high-visibility gilets stand at the towing point of Paul's boat. Three are watching one of them (the bar owner?) cutting. No sense of urgency in the tableau of heads bent over the task. No look-out. At one point, the cutter – it is the man from the bar – glances up at the four faces staring down from *La Chamade*.

The boat snaps free. The men grasp the bar and jolt the craft clear of the pavement. Before they can take up their positions at the rear of the trailer, Paul's boat is rolling towards the sea. They give it one hard push and wait until it crashes off the slipway onto the rocks.

From inside the house, Esther and her children hear wood splintering on stone.

Esther envisages the cream and turquoise shell askew on fringes of algae slime.

'We ought to phone the police,' she says.

The children have gone back to their good works in the sun.

By the time the police call, Paul has hauled the remains of his boat from the harbour. He doesn't want to press charges, make accusations.

'They did it on purpose,' Esther says. 'We saw them.'

'They had to do something. To make themselves men of consequence. In their eyes, I have never been punished.'

For days, he breaks the boat into manageable pieces, stacking the components at the back of his garage. Esther notices he is strict with himself about what is salvageable and what is rubbish. Shattered scraps of timber, he decides, will make a beach bonfire.

'Is it allowed? To have fires on the shore?'

'Probably not.'

He invites Esther to join him at the pyre.

'We should light it early morning when the sky is still dark above the horizon. Fewer people will notice. And by the time the ashes have cooled, we'll be able to see clearly to gather up the mess.'

Paul agrees.

'Bright blue boats burn best before breakfast,' says Esther. 'Seven alliterative words for luck.'

The fire whooshes high with a dose of petrol. Paul and Esther sit at the foot of the dunes until it dies down.

'Are you sad? I've still got my dogs but your boat has gone.'

'The boat was my cross, my millstone, my dung of the dung beetle.'

'Always? Or since the accident?'

'What did they tell you about the accident?'

'Nothing. My children heard the story from somewhere in the village. Seven people died.'

'My wife and our two daughters were among the seven. That is the first time I've said it aloud.'

Esther took his hand. His fingers were rough and bloodstained from building the bonfire.

'She was like you, a gatherer. Berries, wild sorrel, wild garlic, all manner of low tide creatures. She didn't trust supermarkets. Toxic cupboards, she said. I indulged her. She was a local girl. I was the outsider with city ways. I trusted her knowledge. I was a fool.'

'Unlucky.'

'Unlucky! That puts tragedy in its place.'

Esther and Paul make love in a hollow of the dunes. They go by different paths back to their houses.

Esther's dogs, bored during her absence, have pulled the silky belt from her dressing gown, shredded the tassels and bitten the pink and orange braids into a mess of salivary threads. Destroyed, it still glows on the bare boards of her bedroom floor. In that moment, Esther recognises it as part of a woman's garment. She rescues it from Lark and Spur, forms it into a ball and drops it in an empty drawer at the bottom of her wardrobe.

Let the weeds wither. Sweep rooms for the guests.

DIMA ALZAYAT

Disappearance

The summer Etan Patz disappeared, New York was burning something fierce. 'It's hotter than a hooker in hell', my father would say after a day's work, his collar slack and soiled, his scalp like wet sandpaper.

For three months our mothers kept us indoors, wouldn't let us out no-way-no-how, convinced that the man who'd snatched Etan was prowling the neighbourhood for more. I imagined a lunatic in a sorcerer's cap stirring a pot of boys with a broom handle, bending over and pinching their thighs to feel for tenderness. Wondered what we'd smell like in that pot. Probably something awful, all that Kool-Aid and Play-Doh, gym socks and rusted pennies, pooled together like that.

'Let me out woman,' I'd demand each morning and duck in time to miss my mother's palm swinging towards the back of my head. I hated her then in those moments, my larger-than-life warden, wide and rubbery like an inflatable raft sheathed in floral cloth. Why I had to be kept from the swimming pool, stickball games and sugar cones balancing scoops of rainbow sherbet, I didn't understand. She never budged, not once. Stayed like that too, the rest of her life, unyielding as a nail in cement, until we buried her. Even then, at the very end, she'd still go on about 'Poor Etan.'

Only thing that kept me from grabbing a bed sheet and parachuting out the window that summer was Tommy Palansky. He'd moved into the apartment beneath ours and his mother wasn't letting him out either. We'd spend every morning running up and down the stairs of our four-storey building, the light filtering in through ceiling panes thick with dust and falling across us in streaks of grey. We'd gather Legos, rubber balls, wadded newspaper, candles melted down to their stubs, old slippers – anything we could filch undetected. Then we'd position ourselves on the steps on either side of the stairwell and build military posts out of broken-down cardboard boxes and plastic tubs and declare War with our ragtag arsenal. My brother Ralph would stand in the doorway and watch, drooling all over himself and saying nothing.

'Ben, let Ralph play with you,' my mother would holler from the living room where she sat peeling potatoes or snipping green beans into a colander, the record player behind her always screeching nothing but Cher.

'All he does is drool, ma,' I'd yell back. I'd hold real still then, listening for the creak of wooden baseboards beneath her swollen feet. Sometimes she'd leave me be a little longer but eventually she'd come, her weight pressing down on linoleum and thudding across the cement of the stairwell. She'd pinch my ear between fingers, plump and damp, and pull me so close I could make out the short black prickles sprouting from her chin.

'His whole life people gonna look to us to see how they oughta treat him,' she'd say. But the kid really did drool everywhere, spit that mixed and mingled with all the other fluids he leaked. Sweat and snot and saliva on his face and neck, t-shirts, every Tonka truck and green army man we owned. The heat made it worse. He'd wake up dry enough and by lunchtime he was like a sponge left in a bucket of dirty water.

Rubbing my ear, I'd take his hand and lead him to my post, prop him up on the front line and hand him artillery to launch at Tommy. He was good at taking orders from me when he was in the mood for it, I had to give him that. Would strike Tommy on the shoulder with empty shampoo bottles and right on the head with wooden blocks.

'That's not fair there's two of you now,' Tommy would groan.

'Pipe down. He's like half a damn person,' I'd say. Then Tommy would get bored and start crawling on all fours, hooting and roaring and pounding his chest like a mad gorilla or some other wild beast. He'd circle Ralph like that, coming close enough to sniff him and then retracting in disgust. Guess I couldn't blame him. The kid smelled like pickled eggs most days. Ralph never would react. He'd just stare right ahead and you couldn't be certain if he was actually seeing Tommy or even looking, and back then I didn't know there was a difference. I can't say I felt bad for him then the way my mother did. Didn't see any sense in feeling bad for someone who didn't seem to mind.

'What do you think he thinks about?' Tommy asked. I couldn't guess what went through Ralph's mind any more than I could name what was broken in the first place. I was three when he was born and my mother would say I spent a couple of years just waiting for him to get up and play. I'd try giving him my newest Hot Wheel, my best Transformer, even tucked a pillowcase into the back of his collar so we could make like superheroes and fly. But he never had a want for any of that. Sure enough he got up and learned some words but his eyes, they just didn't move like

40

ours. It was like we were nothing more than stagehands to him and he was waiting for the show to start.

By noon the stairwell would get too hot to bear and we'd escape to the basement then, where walls of exposed brick escaped the sun's reach and remained cool to the touch. Except for a few empty trunks and a lone chair there was nothing much else in the space. Sometimes our mothers would let us carry down a couple of fans and we'd set them up near opposing walls and position Ralph in the centre. Then we'd veer and tilt around him like jet planes, spreading our arms and letting the breeze make its way through our thin t-shirts, drying our underarms and sending shivers down our spines.

Spent, we'd collapse onto the floor and talk about our dwindling summer in captivity and the encroaching start of another nine months spent in classrooms that smelled like mildew and vinegar. 'Is he ever gonna go to school?' Tommy asked once about Ralph. I didn't answer. My father had wanted Ralph to go to school, even tried enrolling him in Special classes for a few weeks the year before. Then some kid scratched him up pretty bad, pressed a pencil with a broken tip down into the soft flesh of his wrist and dragged it up and down his forearm until the skin broke. All that afternoon Ralph said nothing about it. Sat through the rest of his classes and dinner, even watched some *Tom and Jerry* with me. It wasn't until she undressed him for a bath that my mother saw the carved skin, the dried blood flaking off like red ash. That's when she stomped her foot down and said No More. She got approval to home school him then, but not before she clomped down the stairs and the three blocks to school and made every school official cower or cry.

Without fail our basement conversations would soon turn to Poor Etan. Whole afternoons we spent imagining what happened to him. Six years old, same as Ralph, and he goes missing the first time he walks alone to the bus stop. How's that for luck? We imagined him holed in a basement like ours, tied up and invisible to the world. Sometimes we'd really get on a roll and invent entire scenarios. We imagined him stoned to death and buried alive. Burned in a fire as an offering to some cult god, lit at the feet so his screams grew in pitch as the flames surged upwards. We imagined him skinned and hanging in one of the meat shops in Chinatown, like a rabbit waiting to be fried or baked for dinner. I could always picture it so perfectly then. His photo was on the news each night and on the cover of my father's paper each morning. I knew his face better than I knew anyone else's, maybe even my own. Hair blonde and long like a girl's.

41

Eyes wide-set and blue. A smile that cut into his cheeks and spread past his lips, a smirk to maybe say it was all a joke, that at any moment he'd reappear.

Sometimes we'd bring down some twine and take turns tying each other to the chair and pretend that one of us was Etan and the other the kidnapper. Ralph'd just drool and watch. Our weapons of combat would transform into devices of torture and we'd pretend to slit each other's throats and ply fingers off one by one while yelling things like, 'Gimme all your dough', and, 'Where's the cash stash, punk?' We knew a kidnapper wasn't gonna ask for money – but we couldn't quite figure what it was he would ask for, what it would be he was after, so we carried on like that. My mother found us once, after I'd tied Tommy good and tight to the chair and was threatening to zap him from here to Jupiter with my plastic gun if he didn't tell me where he'd hidden the goods. She nearly tore us to crumbs but my father who was just getting home and in no mood for a fight said, 'Darla, they're like caged ferrets. You gotta let them have a tumble every now and again.' Still, she told Tommy's mother and made me carry the fan upstairs. But by the end of that week we were back down there and at it again.

When we were feeling really daring we'd creep down to the ground floor, a small open space that housed abandoned bicycles and the door to the outside. I'd drag Ralph along so he wouldn't tell on us and Tommy would twist the metal latch and pull the door, thick and hulking, so we would stick our heads out one by one into the humid air. Soon enough we began daring each other to step out onto the pavement, to walk to the corner where the Guatemalan man sold fresh fruit and cigarettes, and eventually, to sprint full speed around the entire block once if not twice. Even now, more than thirty years later, I can remember the way the warm air filled me as I ran, how it surged and swirled in my lungs before making its escape and demanding to be replaced. I must have passed the fruit stand then and taken a right, ran past *Earl's Drugs and Stuff* and the video store, turned right again and rushed past *Didi's Donuts*, the hot dog cart and the laundromat. That must have happened but I couldn't tell you then what I was passing, the streets feeling new and foreign even though I'd walked them all the years of my life, had known nothing but their shapes and colours. Instead, I made out the curves of lips and angles of noses, the arches of brows and lines of grimaces. A bald man with a diamond ear-stud leaned on a shuttered butcher shop, a suit in a fedora brushed my arm as he passed, another wearing nothing but shorts and sneakers bounced a basketball as he went. I ran fast enough so I didn't look at any one of them directly, couldn't tell you the colours of their eyes, but knew that they could look towards me, could see me if they wanted. As I rounded the final corner, I'd erupt into something of a frenzy, an invisible current coursing through my veins, leaving me feeling at once fearless, like I could do anything, and relieved that I wouldn't because someone was waiting for me to return.

I can't tell you exactly what day it was that Ralph went missing. I just know it was the week before we started school and the sun was low enough to turn everything orange.

Tommy's parents had gone to visit a relative in Queens and my mother had offered to watch Tommy until after dinner. I never invited my school friends home in those days and a sleepover was unthinkable. The one time I did have someone over, this kid Joey, Ralph drooled all over the Chinese checkers Joey'd brought with him and during dinner, kept his mouth clamped tight while my mother tried to feed him steamed carrots and rice. By the end of the meal, his face was covered in orange pulp and Joey was staring at him like he was a zoo exhibit. The next day the entire class was talking about it.

Sure Tommy wasn't especially keen on Ralph always hanging around, but he knew Ralph, knew what that meant and didn't mean, what it said and didn't say. When I found out Tommy would be eating with us, I begged my mother not to make whatever trendy concoction she'd picked up from one of her cooking shows. It was 1979 and exotic sounding dishes with names like South Sea Beef and Chicken Tahitian were all the rage – culinary experiments that ended with my father sweating just trying to keep them down and Ralph spitting half-chewed chunks onto his plate until she caved and made him a hot dog.

That night though, she'd agreed to Spaghetti Bolognese and the smell of crushed garlic and simmering tomato sauce wafted down to Tommy and me as we stood on the ground level of the building, bent over with hands on knees, panting. We'd already run around the block three times each while Ralph sat and played with his plastic trucks.

'Come on, Ben. Just let him go once.' Tommy said, still gasping for air.
'Why?'
'Because I'm bored just doing the same old thing.'
I shrugged. 'We could play Legos.'

'Oh, come on. He wants to go, don't you Ralph?' Tommy looked to Ralph who had picked up a truck down to its last wheel, was flicking the wheel with his finger to make it spin.

'It's almost dinnertime,' I said. 'Anyway, he won't do it.'

'Sure he will, he'll do anything you say if you're the one to say it.'

Ralph glanced up to me just then and I remember searching for something in that look, for a twitch or a well-timed blink. Anything. But on it went, that endless gaping stare.

'See?' Tommy said. 'He's just waiting for you to say it.'

I stood there for what must have been no more than a minute but it felt like all of time was stretched before me, pulled like silly putty in all directions at once. My ears burned and I knew my face would follow. I remember wishing he would just say something, that he'd open his mouth and a 'Yes' or 'No' would make its way out of his garbled brain. I'd heard him speak before, knew he could. But the one time I needed him to, he couldn't. Wouldn't. Instead he sat silent and watching and I felt my insides grow hot, like someone had lit a match in my stomach and left it to burn.

'Fine,' I said. 'Ralph, run around the block one time.' Tommy let out a small yelp and pulled open the heavy door. Ralph slowly rose and walked towards it, never breaking my gaze as he moved. I hoped then that he would just turn around and run up the stairs instead, decide to watch television or cling to my mother's skirt as she cooked, anything. See, I'd say, I told you he wouldn't do it.

But he did. He walked through the door and took the five steps down to the sidewalk, squinting his eyes to adjust to the light. And then I knew it was actually happening, that Ralph was gonna run around the block alone, be outside alone for the first time, and I just wanted it to be over. 'Run fast, Ralph. Around the block okay?' I said. 'Just fast and around the block.' But he was no longer looking at me, had stepped outside and turned his eyes to sky and sidewalk.

He had just taken off towards the fruit stand, his arms stiff at his sides but his stride certain in its direction, when I heard my mother bellow my name from upstairs. Tommy shook his head, signaling me to ignore her. But again she called, louder this time and I knew she'd come barreling down those stairs, her legs thick and bowed like a charging bull's, if I didn't answer. I stood in the doorway and could see Ralph turn the corner and escape the reach of my voice as I called to him. Again, my name left my mother's lips and echoed in my ears. Tommy was now pushing me towards the stairs, knowing we'd both be punished something awful if we were discovered.

I took the steps two at a time and found her bent over the television. 'I wanna move it to the kitchen, Ben. Tired of all this walking back and forth.' If she had looked at my face for even an instant she would've known right then and there what I'd done but she was struggling to get a firm hold of the thing. 'Come on Ben, try to get the other side.' It was heavy, that television, the kind built into a wooden console as if it didn't have a right to exist alone, had to be a piece of familiar furniture first. It was too cumbersome to pick up but impossible to push. Our difference in size didn't help either. Even after getting it up, we had to put it down and re-lift every few steps. The sweat stood on her brow and her dress clung to her like saran wrap. I would've felt sorry for her if I wasn't so worried about the trouble I'd be in if she knew. During our final rest she asked after Ralph and I told her he was on the stairs with Tommy. I pretended I knew that for certain. Wanted to believe I knew that for certain. Enough time had passed.

When we'd finally moved the damn thing into the kitchen, just as she raised her head and turned her eyes to meet mine, I made for the door. 'Fetch Ralph and Tommy and come back up here. That's enough for one day.' I left without answering, nearly fell twice running down, slipped and slid down the last few stairs. When I got to the ground floor, the big door was shut. I stood there a moment, confused, even turned around and looked back at the staircase, somehow expecting to find Tommy and Ralph standing there, waiting. But I was alone.

I pulled open the door and though I'd not been gone all of maybe fifteen minutes, already the light was changing – the way it grows brighter right before it turns purple and disappears altogether. To my right a couple stood, arguing. The man was calling the woman names that to this day I don't like to repeat and she was swinging at him as he cursed. The man started to turn towards me so I glanced past him towards the fruit stand where a mother paid for a bag of mango slices for her daughter, lit a cigarette for herself. I turned my head in the other direction but aside from a mangy cat rummaging through the trash, the sidewalk was empty. Taxis and cars honked at one another on the street, their headlights turning on pair by pair as the light faded. My chest felt tight and flat, like the whole of the sky was pressing down on it in, like I was no more than God's rolling board.

I stepped out onto the pavement and heard the door slam behind me before I realized that I had no way back in without buzzing my mother.

The arguing couple was walking away now and the mother and daughter were crossing the street. I scanned the sidewalk in both directions two, three times and just started running towards the stand, rounded the corner and picked up speed. Everywhere I looked, my eyes sought Ralph, tried to remember what colour shirt he was wearing, whether it was blue or green, the one with Batman or the Joker. I began to feel faint and sick like when you eat too much or not enough, like I was full and empty all at the same time.

I ran until I realized I'd circled the block three times and each time I saw new faces and the same faces but with something new about them. A scarred cheek, crooked teeth, sunburned skin. I looked them directly in the eyes, searched for some clue as to where Tommy and Ralph had gone, as to who had seen them, who had taken them. On my fourth time around, the Guatemalan had started to pack up his goods and nodded to me as I passed.

With each step I took, what light remained seemed to scatter even faster, eager to leave the world or at least my part of it, and I became less afraid of what my mother would do to me and more frightened for Ralph and what the sorcerer would do to him. I remember wishing that something big would happen, like a tornado or an earthquake, just so it would be bigger than what was happening then. The only thing that kept me from screaming right there on the sidewalk was that I had to keep running. That, and I knew Tommy had to be with him, that Tommy would follow that sorcerer to his dungeon and save Ralph, and Etan too. He'd free them and tie up the sorcerer in their place.

Thirty minutes later, I sat on the kitchen floor, huddled in a corner while police officers went in and out of the apartment, their radios buzzing with codes only they understood. My father had gone out with a search group on foot, scouring the neighbourhood. Tommy's parents had returned; his mother stood in the hallway outside our apartment screaming at the cops to go find her son while his father sat in our kitchen with his head in his hands.

Over and over the same police officer kept asking me to repeat the story, how I'd left Tommy and Ralph on the ground floor, that maybe we had opened the door to let in air, that maybe we had taken turns just going outside for a few minutes at a time. The questions kept coming – the same ones with the words rearranged, until my mother turned to the officer and said Stop. But even then she wouldn't look me in the eye. That's how I remember my mother to this day, though she'd live another twenty years before dying from too many cigarettes. She kept pressing the thumb of one hand into the palm of the other, pressed so hard I thought she'd push a hole right through. She stopped only to hold up a picture of Ralph the cops had asked to see. 'No, he's not blonde. It was the light in the photo studio. Made everything look different.' She kept repeating.

Neighbours showed up in turn at our door offering to pray with us and though I never knew my mother to miss a Sunday mass, she told them they'd be more useful walking the streets, searching. But I prayed anyway. Jumbled together Hail Marys and Our Fathers, promised to give Ralph my toys, to never want another thing again if only he'd appear. At some point, a cop asked me to come down to the landing, to show him exactly where we were playing, to describe who stood where and when. I looked to my mother and though she nodded, still her eyes refused mine.

A few cops stood on the ground level of the building, the door now wide open. I could make out a news truck and reporters, more cops and neighbours. One of the reporters, a blonde woman in a red blazer noticed me then and rushed towards the building. The cops quickly filled the doorway and stood between us. Still, I could see her peering over their shoulders as other reporters joined her – a mass of shifting microphones and cameras and voices. The officers ordered them to step away from the door and pulled me back but not until I heard one of them ask if I'd witnessed the disappearance.

When the cops found Ralph tied up in the basement, my mother let out a cry so loud and terrible, a long howl that waned into a low moan. They walked in on Tommy holding the plastic gun and Ralph's head welted where Tommy'd struck him with it. Ralph sat shirtless in that chair, his arms and legs bound, his *Fantastic Four* tee gagging his mouth. Dried tears ran in streaks down his neck and his pants were soaked, the stench of piss filling the room. When the cops walked him through the door of the apartment and into my mother's arms, he turned to me for no more than an instant and though his eyes neither twitched nor blinked, I understood them.

To this day, I don't know what became of Tommy. His parents moved out the next day and the apartment stayed empty for months. That night, my mother bathed Ralph for nearly an hour while my father stood in the doorway and watched over them both without speaking. I sat in the hallway, waiting, until my father turned to me and said it was time for bed.

I lay in the darkness and looked across at Ralph's empty bed, wondered what Etan's bed looked like, empty like that, night after night. I waited for what felt like hours and crept out of bed and down the hallway. My parents' bedroom door was open and I could see my father asleep in his work shirt. In the kitchen, the spaghetti sat on the table, untouched. I found my mother in the living room, Ralph wrapped in a towel and asleep on her lap. I sat next to her and for hours I couldn't be sure if she was awake or asleep, her breaths low and far in between, her eyes difficult to see in the darkness. Then, at around dawn, when the shadows in the room began to shift and I could make out her face and she could make out mine, she pulled me towards her.

BENJAMIN DIPPLE

mice story, not his

shhhhhhhhhhhhh!
if you stand still long enough in this house,
and I do mean still, because
any movement, on any floor,
in any room, will make the boards cry out,
Literally
they will laugh and scream at you
(although when I was living here
I didn't even notice it.
weird that)

when I was younger I once called the floors our bulgar alarm. this cute
middle class joke stuck as it combined the adorable confusions of an only
daughter (me) and my dad's belief that humour would keep the bad things
away (and yes I was adorable once, I think we all were, weren't we?)

well ha ha bonk. the joke is well and truly upon us now

on us, or upon us?   onus. anus. annus. annus horribilis. anna's horrible
lisp. I don't know an anna but I know ananas is pineapple in french and
not banana like you might think. I don't know about you. but I think, it's
one of the few enjoyable things that you can do by yourself that doesn't
make you go blind, unfortunately us girls aren't supposed to do either of
them

I've forgotten what I was saying

the floorboards!   yes, the sneaking creaking floorboards. yes, if you
stand still long enough in this house, you can actually hear the mice living
in the walls. at night, when everyone else has gone to bed, and finished
sucking and fucking and all that stuff, you can actually hear the mice
crawling up and falling down the insides of the walls. they have created

entire road networks in the old plaster – or should that be partial road networks? as they are constantly burrowing new tunnels that means they haven't finished what they are doing, or they aren't satisfied with it, therefore they haven't created an entire network, as entire means complete. doesn't it?

anyway, I've been standing here for ages, I don't know how long exactly as although I can see a child's clock all I can make out is a picture of the moon, like she couldn't work that out by herself, so I don't know how long I have been in her bedroom, but in that time I haven't heard anything. the mice seem to have gone and I didn't take them with me

we used to have a cat which we purposely never fed hoping it would eat them up, and we had plug-in whiny things that were supposed to scare them away, but you had no idea if they were working or not or if someone had just sold you a black plug for twenty quid, or however much they were, I never bought them, I didn't give a shit about the mice, they weren't part of my life, basically I just ignored them, but mum and dad had poison and traps everywhere and every time someone came round to buy the house we had to hide them and when they asked if we had any trouble with vermin, we said no. or mum and dad said no, no one ever asked me which is pretty stupid of them as I would have said yes, we have mice, tons of the things, but they never did because I am a kid and apparently, kids are thick

so my bedroom is the same, i.e. the door and the window are where they used to be and so are the floor and the ceiling and also the walls. (this isn't so 'durr!' I've been to houses where all of these things were moved because of some new television DIY thing, or because in that street houses now cost so much it made sense to ram in an extra bedroom/loo/shower/underground car park/cinema, whatever. and yet you can buy a house up north for a quid). the room is a lot tidier now, even the pictures on the walls are on bits of board made of cork and stuck in with coloured pins (I turned the main light on to get a better look at these, the star night light thing is crap). my blue tack stains have gone, wiped away and painted over, the pictures of x, y and z gone too and replaced with other faces and fantasies. I can't remember mine

a boy, a girl   a boy and a girl   a girl and a girl

the bed is new. I don't know what happened to my old one, we didn't take it with us. why didn't we take it with us? did they sell that too? someone else is lying in the new bed, sleeping so calmly that they can have no idea of the amount of shit in here, out there, in the world, in their life, in my life. else you wouldn't sleep. Ever. Never, Ever

like children. If you knew where they came from, and how, and what they did, and what they did to you, and your life, you wouldn't have them. Ever. Never, Ever. mum said that. she looks younger than me, the girl in the bed (not my mum, god no, these days she looks well rough). the girl looks younger than me even when I was lying there, in her bed, my bed. she looks younger than I can remember being. she must be about ten and I must have been about ten once, but I don't remember it, it's only five years ago and I don't remember what it tasted like, what it smelt like

did it smell, did it taste
I don't think about what it looked like
or felt like. or was like

the girl is moving, turning in the bed and I could almost squeeze in beside her, I could actually lift up the white duvet and slide onto the cotton sheets. I have no idea if they are cotton, but they probably are. I wonder if her pyjamas would fit me, getting into bed with my clothes on seems wrong, but so does climbing in naked. so I look in her drawers, they are nice and tidy, and her pyjamas look like a tracksuit, maybe so she can run at night from whatever is chasing her – and I check her bed to see if she has NIKES on but there are just two pink feet there – and she looks the most untroubled person I have ever seen, nothing is after her, no one is after her, and yet we share the same room, the same address, we could almost be sharing the same life, and maybe she leaves the front door and we follow the same path, to the same shops, the same school, the same end. and I wonder about my old swing, does she use it, is it still here? and so I am getting changed when the door to our bedroom opens

and so we are in the kitchen, me and Mr. X, who is a bit embarrassed (the girl is called phoebe I have found out) and he is making me a hot chocolate while he has a drink, none for me he jokes, I'm too young, and we are talking about how phoebe is getting on at her new school, he's glad she has made a friend he says, apparently she's found it hard to settle, and

51

he didn't realize she was having a sleepover, he has just got back from…, and he says a town but I haven't heard of it and it sounds foreign, yet if I haven't heard of it, how does it sound foreign? Durum sounds foreign, especially when you say it a lot and I can't spell it but it isn't foreign as nan lives there, and I realize they have moved the biscuits in the glass jar because they have moved the cupboards and the cooker and the fridge and in fact the whole fucking kitchen isn't even where the kitchen was which was why I was worried when he took me downstairs to make me a hot drink as there was nothing downstairs before but a rather creepy cellar with bikes that we never rode and cardboard boxes that we never unpacked but now there is a killer kitchen (and I'm not even into that stuff) with a shiny tiled floor that is so warm I can wander around barefoot on it and now there are little brick windows in the ceiling at the front so you could see shoes walking past if it was day and there were shoes walking past and at the back there is a huge glass door that looks out on to the garden and I press my face up to the glass but it is so dark I can't see anything which is a bummer and then a cat sees me and jumps over the fence – probably to get fed by the neighbour like ours did although it isn't our cat and I never found out where she went either – and it sets off the outside lights that never worked when we were here and I can see the garden now and I can see the tree with my old swing still hanging from the branch and I'm almost home

I bet phoebe likes the swing I say and her dad nods and smiles and I nod and smile and I see him looking at me standing by the window sprouting out of the pilfered pyjamas and I explain I forgot mine and he says I must be on the netball team being so tall and I explain they banned me, for being so tall, as I hate netball (I'm not a catcher you see) and I don't want him to ask me what position I play as I might have to tell the truth. sometimes you actually want to tell the truth but you just need someone to ask you the question first, because if you just came straight out with it you would look like a twat

at least he doesn't seem to be perving

at school I live in the loo

I think phoebe actually goes to my school. I thought she'd go to a posh one, seeing as they can actually afford this house, but no. I didn't ask which school she went to, as obviously he thinks I go there, and if I did ask he might suss that I don't go there (if it turns out I don't), and then he might want to know what the hell I am doing in his house, even though he is a bit tired and being a bit thick thinking his daughter – who has Barbies in her room and pictures of horses on those cork board things – could be in the same class with me, who, whilst not being Zoë Hill, has actually blossomed as nan once put it

at school I live in the loo, so therefore phoebe probably never saw me

at school I live in the loo. I piss in it, I shit in it, I bleed in it, I puke in it. hopefully not all on the same day or that would be a bad one. I hide in it, which is ironic as it's where all the shit stuff happens too – it's where my phone got flushed, my head got flushed, my clothes got flushed and where my books got flushed too. I do actually read you see. I'm not stupid. I met K in the loo too. And then she left. she moved school, to a better one, to a nicer one, to a further away one, to a further away from me one, and left me behind, as well as her phone, which is also down the loo. and I wonder if they have a net at the end of the sewer where all the phones collect. I never went to K's house before, though I did go recently. I sat in her swing, watching her bedroom window, watching her turn the light out to go to bed

once I went to Zoë Hill's, and I sat on her swing (nobody has merry-go-rounds in their gardens, just swings, wrong size I suppose) and I watched her pacing up and down in her room without her top on and speaking on her phone (which has probably never been flushed down the loo) and zapping the television with the remote control and smoking a cigarette and I imagined zapping her with a remote control or turning her off using a gun or stubbing that fag out on her face like she did on my arm which seriously hurt and I pissed on her swing and went home wet which sort of defeated the point only if I am being honest I hadn't planned on pissing on her swing it was just that she stood at the window and looked out as if she knew someone was watching her and her massive tits were squashed flat on the glass and I pissed myself

Mr. X is asleep. I get my clothes and go back out the front door, locking it with my old key (the door is huge and ancient and so is the key, the estate agent said it added character, I said which character, he said an old one. we went to an old house once on a bank holiday and everything was set out like a home, only no one lived there). the pyjamas are folded up in the drawer, I briefly think about taking them in case they have my DNA on them but instead I wash my cup up and pour a cap full of whisky on Mr. X's clothes as he snores in the kitchen and then a capful for myself which doesn't even burn anymore and then I leave the open bottle on the table like in a film and I hope he thinks it was a drunken dream, or a ghost, and not that he is going mad

phoebe is actually at my school in year one. I've seen her now, she has no friends and gets bullied a lot and sits at the edge of the playground and when she thinks no one is looking she sucks her thumb

I saw my dad one day, or one night, when I was out
I used to walk along the pavement at night, I love fires
I used to walk along the pavement at night
and look in the windows, and see the burning hole,
the burning whole, the burning red and orange coal,
the blues, the hisses, the black, the wood,
the manna, the warmth, the light, the good,
the tools for prodding, the lighter for lighting,
the baskets of wood and yesterday's newspapers, where
murder and disease and war and GCSE results and all that shit
would be reduced to smoke and soot and ash,
so we could forget them, in time for the next time,
I miss all that

snow had begun to fall. this is probably bollocks but I remember there being snow and what is history but what we remember, even six-month-old history. I am not sure whether this is what Mr. Finnegan at school said or whether he said what I just said was wrong. that history wasn't what we remembered, but what we knew, or recorded, or something. or whether it even mattered. and there was my dad leaning against the wall of the pub, Christmas Eve, trying to get them to let him back in and I said I would take him home and he had no idea who I was and I had no idea where he lived as mum had kicked him out by then and neither did he and so we sat outside until it got too cold and I took him back home and hid him in the cupboard under the communal stairwell that led to our shitty flat and he fell asleep and was gone by the morning leaving only the stink of booze and fags and a pile of piss in the corner – a pile of piss? all the other words sound wrong, a pond of piss, a lake of piss, a river of piss, a sea of piss, a stream of piss – too flowing, too fluid, too melodramatic (I do know what these words mean), when it was just a piss stain, a piss take, a pile of fucking piss. And the next day he fell in the canal and died.

I follow phoebe home. life has got worse for her. a group often waits for her up by the zebra crossing. Zebras, Pelicans, Lollipops. they are up by the newsagents, and she will have to pass them and then follow the road back round on itself to get home. I am now thinking of becoming her big sister, so I decide to act like one. I walk up behind her, she is so dense she doesn't even hear me or look round, and I pull her behind the row of houses and down an alleyway that goes through to the back gardens. she doesn't even scream or ask me what I'm doing but we don't have time for me to shout at her for being such a pillock right now. we turn right and go to the dead end of the back alley, only I know the fence panel there gives way if you push it and we squeeze through into an identical alley the other side, only now it exits into the next street, i.e. the one after the twats on the corner. I put the fence back in place and we go down to the end of the next lot of gardens, about thirty houses worth, all tucked in together, and I take off her blazer and switch it round and do the same to mine, it looks crap but from a distance the black lining looks like the catholic school nearby not the green of our school so even if they spot two figures they might not guess it was us and when we come out we don't even go down the road anyway we just run across it and down the lane opposite and take the long cut back and when we get home she invites me in for tea

this is the thing. I was her, but it was in reverse really. all the time I lived at our house they never took the piss. I was a muppet at sports and said weird things in class and had shaved hair but I managed to avoid their attentions, but then dad went bust and made an idiot of himself at the bank, who weren't fucking listening then, and got himself in the paper and it all kicked off, the bullying at school, me and my stuff getting flushed down the bog, and then when I got home the facebook shit would be waiting for me, and so it went on, until he fell into the canal and I jumped out of the window

after that it sort of stopped. mum did go ballistic at the school when she found out, so maybe that helped, or maybe that was enough for me, not so much job done as just no more job left to be done, so move on, carry on with life, only I can't, I'm stuck there with my legs in the air. and now phoebe gets the piss taken, because she lives in the house, because she is a rich girl, and at the moment that is not cool, and admittedly the horsey magazines don't help, so basically, I am thinking that if we swapped places we would solve both our problems. her mum is nice, mine probably would be too if I didn't give her so much grief, so it could be a win/win situation all round

oh yeah, phoebe's dad reckons the house is haunted. that's the mice I say and she says what mice, and I say the ones in the walls or have you managed to get rid of them and she still looks confused and I realize I am being a bit of a pillock as she doesn't know she's staying in my house so I shut up and she says her dad even had a conversation with a ghost girl in the kitchen and I LOL

I didn't quite work out what he did, but it was hard work phoebe said, and he was away a lot. I asked whether he was a coal miner, they worked hard, and she asked what a coal miner was and I said how the hell should I know, my dad was a builder/property developer, depending on who was asking and how much money was in the bank. I began to show her all the routes home, how some took ages but were safe and I told her about mixing them up, not going the same way two days running and how to get out of school through different doors and that eventually they would get bored and find someone new (or old. this thought did occur to me)

if you haven't ever gone out and about at night I seriously recommend it. apart from the dangers of being attacked, raped, murdered and run over, or mistaken for a prozzy and then being attacked, raped and murdered and run over, it is quite good fun. you meet different people, not many you would want to chat to, most you wouldn't even want to look at, but it's good to know they are there – you can't just hide from them or pretend they don't exist. I used to go out so I could smoke a spliff before bed, a neighbour had grassed me up when he saw the orange glow in our garden as he was cleaning his teeth – to be fair he thought I was a burglar or a pervert – so I went walking, which you have to do fast whilst smoking so you can leave the cloud of dope behind you, then those following you smell it but it's too late as you are miles away in the distance and those passing you don't notice it until too late as you are well gone by then, it's a bit like the sonic boom of those planes going faster than the speed of sound, we did that in science, they leave their own noise behind, well I leave my own shit behind, only you can't really, can you, a little bit of it will always stick to you

after my attempts at flying I couldn't walk like that for a while so I had to use other people's gardens to smoke in, preferably those with unlocked gates and swings in them. I would sometimes go back later and explore a bit (most houses are surprisingly easy to get into – bolts you can open via a cat flap, dog flaps you can just crawl through, keys left under the mat, etc...) I would just go in and wander, sort of like a school project, to see another person's house, another person's home

once I watched a whole film. I didn't mean to, but I knew the house was empty – the calendar in the kitchen had ON HOLIDAY IN GREECE written across it with one of those fluorescent pens, like they would forget what life was if they didn't write it down – so I made a cup of tea, no milk obviously but they had sugar so it wasn't too bad, and I sat and watched a bit of television and IT'S A WONDERFUL LIFE was on and I've never seen it before so I stayed

phoebe was a bit upset today. I am thinking more au pair than sister now, as to be honest, I am putting in a lot of hours and she's a pain in the arse, and then I could actually get paid for this. I did suggest it to phoebe's mum and she laughed. she's all right she is. she said it wasn't a bad idea as things were a bit difficult at home right now, they were having trouble sleeping – I just about stopped myself from saying I know, I could hear you arguing about it the other night (that was when I took the keys to his VW phaeton as well as all their landline phones and put them in the bin down the road. I hoped they would ring them and someone would open the bin to answer them and say hello this is the bin speaking but then I realized they would have been out of range). I've been in their bedroom before, but only when they were sleeping. I heard them having sex once. they'd been arguing, really screaming at each other, then crying, then they fucked. and teenagers are the ones who are supposed to be emotionally messed up

show me the way to go home, I'm tired and I want to go to bed.
I had a little drink about an hour ago and its gone right to my head.
Dad used to sing that, as a joke

57

humans have to be the cruellest people in the world and kids the cruellest humans. I can see phoebe now – they have gathered around her and are opening her bag, tossing the contents onto the grey playground. she has actually brought a horsey magazine to school, I can see it in their hands, even when I specifically told her not to, I even bought her a copy of BEATZ. just put it in your bag, I said, in case they check, and stick to playing my little pony when you get home, which she says she doesn't play anymore, completely missing the point as usual

it is weird watching it. I can see them ripping up her magazine, but beyond that I can see when my own bag was emptied, my own books trashed. I chased GIRL MEETS BOY round the playground until I had most of the words and could stick it back together, so next time they flushed my books down the loo, the words swelling in size before they choked each other to death, yet watching it now like a repeat of FRIENDS when you know all the lines it just becomes dull, and I begin to look in my pocket for some gum

last time this happened to phoebe I missed it, but she bravely collected up all the bits and we spent two hours sticking the whole thing back together at her house and then she went to put it safely away in our bedroom and her mum was crying on the phone to someone and I sat in my usual chair in the kitchen and thought about waking up there, in my house. it was quite nice. I imagined I had just left the marital bed with Mr. X snoring, which he does (I don't know how his wife puts up with it, I'll have to use earphones), and I was getting breakfast ready for him and phoebe and they'd come down and we'd eat and then I'd go out shopping and phoebe would piss off to horse club or something and Mr. X would read the paper and I'd come home with big bags of clothes and he'd want to see them and we'd probably have to have sex but he sounded fairly quick and vanilla and then he'd have to go to work, because he'd have to work weekends to pay his wife's alimony, and then I would be alone in the house at last, and I would clean my teeth, and put on my pyjamas, and climb into my old bed, because, to be honest, I've sort of had enough now – I want to go to sleep, I've had enough. and now that the mice are gone

how do you kill a ghost, how do you bury the dead,
how do you get over what you have lost,
how do you get home safely, swim?
what is the difference between a house and a home?

there is a flash of a camera on a phone on a hand on a person, cutting through the playground gloom, cutting through me, and cutting into phoebe, who is screaming in her ring of hell, yet watching from afar I can also see the door out, my door, her door, our door, but it seems a shit answer

the horses are stumbling at the hedges, the huge green oval leaves catching them in flight and I remember the English lesson when we did the poem of Icarus falling into the water and the teacher tensed up and the whispering started and I knew exactly what they were laughing about so I thought fuck it and I opened the window and jumped out. I tried to fly. I tried to see if I could go faster than the sonic boom, to see if I could leave all this shit behind, and instead I made it as far as the green hedge before the splash

they didn't give a shit as i lay there, legs in the air, so why should i? but that seems shit too and i'm not sure now what to give a shit about, but surely something, or should we all just drown instead

what about Mrs. Icarus?

and I can hear the birds laughing as phoebe is taken inside and the teacher, for some reason, tells me to clear this mess up and I can see phoebe's fingers clutching a horse and I laugh, not at her,
but
      at
          all
              of
                  this
and I jump off my swing and run round after the floating horses, trying to save them, gathering them up for phoebe, her precious horses

her horses

horses, houses, mouses, mices

I do wonder where they went and whether they took their hats with them

59

BARRY LEE THOMPSON

So Much Lemonade

The boy sat down on a shady patch of grass at the side of the car. He watched his parents unload bags and a blanket from the boot. His sister remained seated in the car.

He looked to the edge of the cliffs, then the line of the horizon.

"Did we remember the napkins?" said his father.

"Is she going to sit in the car all afternoon?" said his mother.

"She can sit if she wants," said his father, low-voiced and kindly, with a glance towards the girl.

"She's sulking." His mother soured her face, like a clown. "Is she? Are you sulking? Like a little baby?"

"I'm not sulking," said his sister from the car. She was addressing the mother but looking at the boy, so the tenderness of her expression didn't match the acid in her voice. "I'm tired. Tired, and bored."

The boy studied her face. Her hair hung just short of her shoulders; her nose, though she often described it as ugly and stubby, was neat and petite.

His father spread the rug onto the patch of grass behind the car. He stood back, then lifted a corner, pulled it tighter, and put his fist on his hip.

"Which way's the sun?" he said.

The boy looked up and around. The sky was as bright as a clean towel; the shoreline was hidden by the cliffs, but audible; the sea was solid and unmoving at the horizon.

"There must be toilets here somewhere," his mother said, scanning all along the edge of the cliffs.

"Yes," said his father. "I saw some where we turned onto the grass."

His mother, who'd been taking lids off plastic containers, stopped, a lid in her hand, frowned, and said, "Oh?" She seemed surprised at receiving a response. She looked the other way, and shielded her eyes from the sun. She sighed. "I'll go after lunch. I can hold on."

The car door was open. His sister had shifted herself in the seat, so that one of her bare feet was on the grass. She was wriggling her toes in the cool green blades. Her skirt had ridden higher, so that her upper thighs

60

were exposed, milky and smooth. She had an unlit cigarette in one hand, a lighter in the other, and she seemed to be as far away as the horizon over the cliff-top.

She noticed him staring, and gathered her expression. "Let's go for a walk," she said, low and kindly, like his father earlier. Her eyes were bluer than the sea, and as resigned. "We'll take our time. And maybe we won't come back." She laughed. "If only it were just you and me," she said, leaning in to him. "Things'd be much easier." She slid out of the car, smoothed her skirt over her thighs, and grabbed his hand. "I'm taking him for a walk," she said over her shoulder.

"He's not a dog," said his mother.

"Come on," chided the father, shooting the mother a glancing blow.

"Anyway," said the mother, "we're about to eat. You can wait till after we've had lunch."

"Bloody hell," said his sister, but the words got lost in the wind before his mother could catch them. She hesitated, as if she might be considering going for a walk anyway, but then, still holding hands, they went back to the car.

On the way to the picnic area, they'd stopped at a service station. The father had wanted to get some coffee. He got out of the car, and shoved the keys into his pocket. "I won't be long," he said.

"I'll come with you," the girl had said. "I could do with a ciggie."

"You might as well turn off the radio," said the mother. "I'm not listening."

"Are you sure you don't want anything?" said the father.

The mother pulled a face. "Nothing for me," she replied, looking straight ahead, out of the windscreen. "I can wait. Until we get there. We're almost there, aren't we?"

"I need a coffee. That's all. I've been driving for over two hours."

"Come on, Dad," the girl called.

He leaned in to switch the radio off. There was a thud as the door was closed. Then it was just the boy and his mother. The air inside the car was very hot, and it made him feel sleepy. He looked at his mother in the passenger seat. She put her head back and closed her eyes. He wished that his sister had taken him with her. He also closed his eyes. Then he fell asleep.

When he woke, his mother was asleep. Her head was turned to the side. He'd never watched her sleeping before, and her lolling head with its open mouth and closed eyes made him frightened.

He looked out of the window. His father and sister were walking back towards the car. He didn't look at his mother again until the car door was open, and his sister was saying, "Been sleeping, Mum?"

The mother ignored her. His father started the car. They carried on with the drive, in silence – no radio, no talking. It didn't take long to arrive. His father had said that you could tell when you were near to the sea. "See how the sky seems to get bigger," he'd said. No one had replied.

His father picked up the rug, shook it, then replaced it further away from the car. He kept fiddling with the corners, lifting, replacing, smoothing.

"Stop fussing," said the mother.

The father's back stiffened, but he carried on.

"After lunch," his sister said to the boy, "we'll go for a long stroll." She angled her face towards the parents, but held the boy's gaze, and raised her volume. "Yes. A long, long, stroll. We'll walk till we get too tired to carry on, and then we'll sleep where we fall, keep each other warm, then wake with the dawn chorus, start again, and keep going."

"Stop it," said the mother. "Stop being so silly."

The father had moved the rug again, and was carefully laying plates and cutlery onto it.

His sister held her expression steady, and continued. "We'll find our way, without any help. Me and you." She picked the boy up, and sat him on the bonnet of the car so they were almost at eye-level. She put her hand on her hip, just like their father had done earlier. Then she lit her cigarette. Blowing smoke away from the boy, she said, loudly, "I could sell my body. I reckon we'd get by." She looked down at her chest, and pushed one of her breasts up from below. She winked.

"Lunch is served," said the father, with a slight bow. "And you can get your own child," he said, lifting the boy off the bonnet.

"I don't want my own," she said. She looked very self-assured with her cigarette and short skirt and so-blue eyes.

"Then what do you want this one for?" he said, holding the boy close to his chest. He smelled of Old Spice and the softness of warm wood. He kissed the boy on his forehead.

"Company," she said, winking at the boy then staring at the father. "Someone to tell my troubles to."

"What troubles?" said his father.

"Well..." she said. "Just troubles. Anyway – he listens to me." She flicked ash from the end of her cigarette. Whitish flecks danced away to the sky.

"Well, I'm sorry, but he's going to keep me company in my old age. Aren't you?" said the father.

Wrapped in Old Spice, strong arms, salt-sweet skin, the boy was content with this design for his life, and nodded.

His sister laughed. "Well, lucky you, Dad," she said. "Lucky you."

Something passed between them, like curtains being parted to reveal a previously hidden interior. The father gave the daughter a sad look, as if there were nothing lucky at all about him.

"Am I to eat all alone?" said the mother. The curtain drew closed.

His father took the boy over and sat him on the rug, in front of a place setting. Then he tickled him just under the armpit, and the boy giggled and rolled over.

"Careful," the mother said. "You'll upset the picnic things."

The boy looked at his father, who, for a tiny space of time, looked like he'd become somebody else.

"Honestly," said the mother. She shook her head.

The sister sat on the rug, and carried on, taunting: "I can see it now, as clear as that car." Apart from the boy, they all looked at the car, as if some part of the girl's thoughts would appear on its shellacked surface. "I'll move away to a different place. Somewhere more... More *everything*. I'll set me and him up in a nice place, somewhere warmer. Byron Bay, maybe."

"Byron Bay," said the mother. "Ha!" Then, "I don't know why you waste your breath on fantasy. And put that out. I can't eat with the smell."

The girl ignored the mother, and looked away to the edge of the cliffs. Then they were quiet. The father spooned potato salad onto the plates, and added thin slices of boiled ham, beetroot and white bread.

The girl threw her cigarette away.

The mother told her to get up and put the cigarette out. "Do you want to be responsible for setting the bush alight?"

For a while they ate in silence. At one point, the father started to tell them about how he used to come here as a boy. "It was exactly the same. I loved it. I used to look forward to it. We came here before we were married." He looked at his wife. "And then after we were married. Quite a few times." He put his plate down. "We stopped coming," he said. "I suppose we didn't find the time anymore. Now, we have the time again. Yes, it's nice to have some time." He looked at the boy. "Time is a blessing. Only the very young have plenty of it, but they're not aware."

The boy was looking intently at his father.

"When was the last time we were here?" said the father to the mother. "Can you remember?"

"Is it important?" said the mother.

"A question with a question, Mum," said the girl.

"No," said the father. "No. It doesn't really matter. I wonder though. I wonder when we last came here. It feels as if we were here very recently. And yet it feels like such a long time ago. It doesn't really matter." The father looked at his daughter. "How about you, Pauline? Can you remember when we were last here? You would have been close to Neil's age."

The sister looked at the father. "I remember coming here. But I don't remember when it was." Then she smiled. "I do remember something, though," she said.

"What?" said the father.

"Well, I remember we arrived here, and it was a beautiful sunny day. A bit like today. But warmer. I wonder how old I was. Anyway. We started to unpack the picnic things. It was a day just like today."

"And you remember it?" said the father.

"Now that you've asked me," she said. "Yes. I remember it."

"She's going to say something funny," said the mother.

"What do you mean?" said the daughter. "What do you mean, Mum?"

"You're going to pull us all along with this, and then you'll throw a bomb into the middle of your story. So we'll all feel bad. Go on, though. Tell us what you remember."

"What's she talking about, Dad?" said the girl.

"Just carry on with your story," he said.

"I don't want to now," she said.

"Oh don't stop on account of me," said the mother.

The girl pouted and sat back, as if she were finished with something.

"Carry on, Pauline," said the father.

"No," she said. "No. I don't want to. It's not really a story. I was just going to say that I remember being here, and the weather. And you were wearing shorts, Dad." She laughed. "Yes! You were wearing shorts. Can we date it from that?"

The father laughed. "It's been a while since I've worn shorts," he said.

"Yes, well. It's best that grown men stay away from shorts," said the mother.

"You looked so good in your shorts," said the daughter. "I remember that."

"Boys wear shorts," said the mother. "Not men."

"Why did you stop wearing shorts, Dad?"

The father said nothing.

The girl looked straight at her mother and smiled wickedly. "Did you tell him to stop wearing shorts, Mum?"

"Men shouldn't wear shorts," she said. "My father never wore shorts. That's how I knew he was a man. He was my father, not my brother."

"Dad," said the daughter, "why did you stop wearing shorts?"

"I don't know," said the father.

"Don't you?"

"No. I just stopped."

"You just stopped."

"That's what your father said," the mother said.

"You just stopped. No reason."

"Do we all need reasons?" said the mother.

"Can't you let him speak?"

"I am here, you know," said the father.

"Then speak," said the daughter.

"You are showing us up, in public," said the mother.

"But there's no one else here, Mum. Not for miles around."

The boy looked around him. They were the only people in sight. He could see the small row of buildings near to the road. They looked like toys, and they wobbled as he stared at them.

"We're the only ones here," his sister said. "No one else. I could scream, and no one would hear me."

"We'd hear you, unfortunately," said the mother.

"I feel like screaming sometimes. I just feel like screaming so loudly. At the top of my voice. Until my throat hurts."

"Don't be ridiculous," said the mother.

The father was watching the daughter very closely.

"Well, I do. Sometimes I feel like screaming."

The boy looked up at one point and his sister was regarding him thoughtfully, as you might a stranger who'd only just walked into a room.

A ladybird alighted onto his mother's foot. As the boy reached out for it, she shrieked, and tried to swat it with her hand.

His sister chewed her food with the look of one for whom nothing that will happen, or might happen, could possibly bring any ounce of joy or surprise. The boy knew this wasn't true of her. She told him many things, when they were alone together: about song lyrics, people she'd seen, colours she liked. She said that he would hear many descriptions of life, from her, from others, and that it was up to him to create his own world. "But you don't understand what I'm talking about, just yet," she said one day. But he did. He understood most of it.

After they'd eaten, his mother stood and regarded the scenery, like a sentinel.

His father began to clear the wares from the rug, whistling in his tuneless way.

"I might want to have some more later," said the mother.

He replaced everything on the rug, and left it as it was.

The sister lit another cigarette and stretched her legs out to where the others had been sitting. She smoked and appraised her feet, turning them at the ankle, this way and that.

The boy also looked at her feet. Her toenails were painted green. She caught him looking and reached out to him, the way he'd tried with the ladybird. She circled him with her ivory arms.

"Are you warm?" she said. He nodded. She clamped her cigarette between her teeth, and took each of his small shoes off, then his socks. His feet felt light and soft in the air. She sniffed one of them, looking at him all the time. "Little boys," she said, "smell so clean. And delicious! I could eat you up. With roast potatoes and bread."

The boy moved pieces of food around the plate with his finger, trying to arrange them into a satisfying shape.

"I think he might become a painter," said the sister. Her white knickers were visible where her skirt had risen.

"Careful, and blow the smoke away," said the mother. She looked nervous, as if an invasion from the sea was imminent, and was wringing her fingers over and over.

"Or a writer," said the girl. "He'll be a writer. He'll write a wonderful novel that will get the whole world talking, and he'll make us all proud."

His father seemed to find this idea very agreeable. "A novel..." he said, hooding his eyes and looking towards the sea.

"And what about you?" said the mother, freezing the girl with a dead stare. "How are you going to make us all proud?"

The father's reverie had been brief.

The girl replied: "Aren't you proud already?"

"Would you be?" said the mother. "If you were me. Would you be proud?"

66

"Now," said the boy's father, as if he were about to announce something. Everybody turned to look at him. For a moment, he had a chance to change things, but perhaps he never intended anything, or if he did, he simply changed his mind.

Either way, all he said was, "Anyone for anymore?" This was one of his phrases. No one answered him.

The boy hadn't finished his cup of lemonade. He picked it up and peered inside. A small fly was swimming on the surface. He touched his finger to the liquid, and the fly swam to it and clung on to his skin. He pulled his finger out, looked at the drowning fly, and then wiped it on his skinny tanned leg. They were all watching him.

"I need to piss," said the girl.

"Pauline," said her father.

"Watch your mouth!" said her mother.

"It's all that lemonade, Dad," she said, standing and wincing. "So much lemonade! We really know how to have a good time. We really do." She looked out at the cliffs again. There was a group of seagulls congregated near the edge, squawking and hopping around. One of them seemed to be facing all the others, a maverick, a leader, or a kook.

The boy followed the noise and her gaze.

"Listen to me," said the mother, slow and pointed. "Watch how you speak." She cocked her head towards the boy.

The girl must have heard her mother speaking, but she had become absorbed, affected by the birds. "It must be so easy," she said, "being a bird. Just flying, looking for food, sleeping. The occasional fight, perhaps. And humans, getting in the way, sometimes."

The boy wondered how his sister knew this. His mother just said, "Don't be ridiculous. You're not a bird, are you?"

The boy noticed his father smiling.

"You're not a bird. You're an adult. It's time you started taking things seriously."

"Oh I do," said the girl. "I take things very seriously. I take everything very seriously indeed, Mum." She was looking right at her mother when she said this, but her mother became perturbed by the girl's stare, or the blue of her eyes, and she quickly looked away.

"I'll be back," said the girl. Then she sang: "*I'll be back, sooner or later, I can't tell you when.*" She brushed bread crumbs from the front of her skirt. The boy was smearing mayonnaise from the potato salad around the edges of his paper plate. She angled her head and frowned, like a connoisseur of fine artworks.

The boy watched her go. She hadn't asked him to go with her. He let the paper plate drop onto the rug.

The mother, seeing that the daughter had gone, took the opportunity to smoke a cigarette. She crossed her arms and watched for the girl coming back.

The seagulls were gone. The boy stood and walked over to where they'd been standing earlier, but the only sign they'd existed was a single grey feather. He stood and watched the feather. He looked back to his parents. The mother was gazing dreamily away to wherever the wisps of smoke took her. The father was beginning to tidy away some of the bits and pieces of their picnic; when they left, later that afternoon, there would be no trace of them ever having been there.

The feather flapped in the wind. He reached out to grab it. As he did, the wind gusted harder, and blew the feather over the edge of the cliff. It floated on the air, level with the boy's head. And then it was snatched away sharply by the wind and carried far out.

The sea below the cliff rolled around, white on blue, and broke on the sand. He watched the waves, and the patterns and colours within the body of water. He felt a curious draw towards the water, its swellings and undulations mesmeric.

He moved closer to the edge: a beautiful sheer drop, like something had been sliced off the land; just salty air and colour. Hovering above it all, like strokes of brilliant white oil paint, enjoying the simple life that his sister had described, was the flock of seagulls they'd watched earlier.

He caught some wind in his hands, and wavered from side to side. He heard his mother say, "Oh Jesus."

"Don't call out," his father said.

"What?"

"Don't call out to him."

The boy smelled his father before he saw or felt him. And then he was in the air, as if lifted by the wind. For a moment he thought that he might be flying.

His father carried him to where the car was, and put him inside, and shut the doors. The boy sat and looked out of the window, and wondered where his sister had gone. It was very warm in the car, and he fell asleep, and when he woke again, they were all in the car, driving along the road. The radio was turned off, and it was dark outside. His sister was filing a nail on her left hand. He watched her for a moment. She didn't look up. She had a very concentrated look on her face, as if she weren't really thinking about her hand or her nail at all. His father suddenly said, "Nearly there." The boy looked at the back of his father's seat, then moved his head slightly to see his hand resting on the gearstick. His mother's head was back on her seat, and she might have been asleep again, but it was difficult to tell. He looked back at his sister, and she peeped out from under her fringe, and smiled a small smile, sweet, and a little bit sad, so that it wasn't like a smile at all. Then his father said, "Yes, nearly there. About ten or fifteen more minutes. It's always good to get home, isn't it?" But no one replied.

MARINELLA MEZZANOTTE

Yesterday's Pies

I may get two meals a day, but I can tell one who doesn't. I see it the moment I open the door, those eyes like wells in her face – it doesn't help that they're so dark – the dry lips, sealed up tight. The mistress doesn't like it, to have a girl get the door, and launches into a speech about "Hobson" being away at his brother's sickbed, even though it's only Mrs Prowse and Miss Allen tagging along after church, as they do most Sundays when the master's not about.

She comes in last after Miss Allen, in an old coal-shuttle of a bonnet with a fraying brim, her face so white I find myself picturing the bottle of salts in the cabinet downstairs. Still, she puts one foot in front of the other and totters after them into the parlour. That hem wants letting down. The whole dress could do with taking in.

Cook and Nancy want to know who it is. Cook's been here the longest, she knows something about everyone comes through this house. I've been here since Michaelmas and I struggle to keep up. I say Mrs Prowse and Miss Allen and she rolls her eyes; as does Nancy, who's only been here since December and never sees anyone unless she's outside when they arrive or leave. But with the master away these three months, they've been round most days, a widow and a spinster without half a life between them. They'll put a healthy girl off eavesdropping, they will.

"Who's the third, then?"

"Shabby girl in half-mourning. Frightful bonnet."

"Mrs Mansfield, dragging the parish poor back from church? *That* bored, is she?"

The way Cook speaks sometimes, she makes me cringe and laugh at once. The mistress is bored, mind, who wouldn't be. One daughter in India with the captain, the other in Egypt with the engineer. Only son at Cambridge studying god-knows-what, as little of it as he can get away with, according to Mr Hobson. The heat doesn't agree with Mrs Mansfield, went to India after she got married and lost her first three babies there, nearly died herself (Cook says – heard it from the lady's maid before last – I wasn't born). Her husband's over there at least half of every year: bound to have a woman, is my mother's guess, children too. But that I won't repeat under Mrs Mansfield's roof, with her husband a rich man and she no flower.

So the mistress may well be that bored, but I don't think the hungry girl's been sent by the parish and I tell Cook and Nancy so. Her boots look worn, but very good, and the ribbons on that bonnet match her gown exactly. Of course, she might have cribbed the boots. The tray is thrust into my hands and I'm sent up to investigate.

"Oh, Nan, speaking of the parish," sighs Cook, shutting the door behind me. I wonder if she means the leftovers, to pack and carry to St George's from the dinner Mrs Mansfield gave yesterday for the visiting society. She wouldn't let Mr Hobson go before that dinner. Three guests cancelled on the day, the pies were not successful, and there's stale bread and cold meat about to turn, as well.

No one looks my way when I walk into the parlour: I can run my eyes over anything and anyone, just as long as I don't fix them. Mrs Mansfield's sitting with her back to the window as she always does when she has company, widow on one side, spinster on the other: there is no girl child in this house or else the shabby stranger might have come to try as governess.

"Very respectable establishment," she gabbles, and if this one's from the rookery, I'm Princess Victoria. "The, the owner cuts most of the patterns and has a boy for errands. Whom *we* hardly ever see. And five of us sewing upstairs, overseen by the one with most experience. A lady in her forties, very ... upright woman." She talks herself into a trembling silence. I slip into the gap between her and Miss Allen, and let my eye slide sideways for a heartbeat. She's not as young as I'd made her out to be: the light catches on a fan of lines above her cheekbone. She dumps a shocking quantity of sugar in her cup and takes a biscuit. I stay for one breath longer than expected and the mistress goes, "Yes, Sally?"

"Begging your pardon, ma'am," I answer in the voice she likes, "Cook is wondering if any of the ladies will be taking luncheon with you today."

"Oh no. Mrs Prowse, Miss Allen and I are expected at the rector's later." She is not telling *me* this. She's telling her. "And Miss Walford is a very busy woman, we mustn't keep her."

There is a tiny clinking from Miss Walford's cup and saucer. She'll have to give her tea another stir soon, all that sugar must be sinking to the bottom even as I stand here.

71

"I shall tell Cook, ma'am." I'm out again and down the stairs. The way she said 'busy'. She picked up that word by the tip of its tail, like a dead mouse.

The tins are out on the kitchen table but Cook and Nancy haven't done a thing, because they got started on the cake and I don't need the second sight to know how much of that will make it to the poor. There's tea for me as well: if Mrs Stevens was loose we wouldn't risk it, but she's upstairs with Lizzie turning all the wardrobes inside out. I feel for Lizzie, missing out on cake, but she does get paid more than Nancy and me together.

"A Miss Walford," I say, and take a sip. "About thirty."

"Colouring?" Cook's eyes are narrow, Nan's are wide.

"Dark. Speaks like the mistress. Seen better days, I'll wager." Cook nods to herself like a Mandarin on a side table; takes some tea, takes some cake, takes her time before she says, "She's not thirty, that one. Can't be twenty-seven. Mother must have died too, if she's in mourning now."

Me and Nancy stuff cake into our mouths at exactly the same time. Turns out this Miss Walford was at school with Mrs Talbot – Miss Dorothy, as was – and they were quite thick for a time, when they were girls, always round each other's house.

"Couldn't eat fish nor go near it, her lips would swell up something terrible. Miss Dorothy saw it happen once, at school, came down specially to tell me all about it when she first invited her. Since then whenever I was told, 'no fish tomorrow, or, no fish next week,' I always knew it was Miss Walford due to visit. Her father made a fortune in the war, I forget how–"

"You forget?" me and Nancy crow as one: she's always teasing us about her memory being sharper than ours, even though she's well over twice our age.

"Yes, yes," and she makes us pay by taking an immense time with her tea and cake. "I forget. For all that matters. He made so much money he bought a house not far from here, might have scraped through without that house. As it is, he lost most of what he'd made, when they were all losing their fortunes, what year was that? The master himself was quite distressed."

"Twenty-five, twenty-six?" I say. I was about ten, then, I remember father trying to explain it all to me. Always read the paper through, did father, all those long words. Perhaps by explaining it to me he explained it to himself.

"That's right, twenty-six. Anyhow, he never picked himself up again after that. He only had the one child living and she was pretty, Miss Walford, very pretty girl and lovely manners. She came down here once, to apologise in person for all that bother with her diet. Lord, her parents must have paraded her around like a prize horse at the time."

Of course, the poor girl would confide in her best friend, who would in turn unburden herself to her own maid. In the end, a man came forward who liked Miss Walford very much, rich enough to give her father a hand-up if it pleased him. She made off the night before the wedding, with a penniless scoundrel she'd danced with a few times.

"But," I say, "she's not married." Nan's exclaiming through her mouthful. Cook clears up our guilty tea things, and sets to piling bread and ham and chicken into a tin. "Two days later she was home again, begging her parents to take her back. It ain't known what had gone wrong with the young fellow. Miss Dorothy got one last letter from somewhere in the country."

I'm staring at a dish of the little veal pies Cook made the other day. She thought she'd make a clutch of small ones instead of one large pie, just for a change, but Mrs Mansfield said they looked like something "the lower orders" might buy in the street. It didn't help that a few came out too crisp and brown, what with so much to do and not enough of us to do it (when the master's due back, she'll take on another girl and maybe one more man). Cook was very upset about the pies.

"But even that is not the end of it," she goes on, her voice dropping to a whisper. "The father went bankrupt, and ... hanged himself." I feel the blood drain from my face. "In his study. No one here had anything to do with the family by then, but one of their maids was employed two doors down after they let the servants go. She said, if Mrs Walford could have afforded to keep the cheapest girl, she never would have known her daughter again. And now. Still not married, and alone. I wonder how the poor girl lives."

"Seamstress," I say.

"Now that's a surprise," says Nancy.

"I don't think she's doing piece work, I heard her talk about a dressmaker's."

Cook ladles soup into the empty tin; I take a napkin to keep my hands fresh for the parlour, and start stacking pies on top of the cold meat. Nan's telling us about a girl she used to know, who couldn't live off shirts and trousers and had to walk the streets at night. "Well," mutters Cook, "she must have saved herself some candles, at the very least." I pick up the last pie. It smells lovely, even cold. Just the thing to make a girl feel better, to walk down the street on a chill, bright spring day taking bites off a delicious pie.

The door opens. Cook and Nan look up, and before I know it I have the pie wrapped in the napkin and inside my apron pocket. Mrs Stevens says, "Ah, Sally. Good. I need you in the bedrooms." My heart's beating so hard it hurts my ears.

"Sally?"

Just then, the parlour bell, like a peal from Heaven (mother will weep with laughter when I tell her this). "Excuse me," I say, and it's all I can do to keep my hands down by my sides as I walk past the three of them. On the landing I take a breath and rearrange the napkin so it peeks out of my pocket, to make sense of the lump. What is the purpose of a housemaid's pocket, after all, if she can't stuff a cloth down it when rung for?

"See out Miss Walford, Sally. Then refresh the tea."

She rises, and curtseys, and cannot thank enough; may the ladies have a pleasant afternoon and should Mrs Mansfield find room enough in her next letter to "dear Dorothy" ... She glides out of the room with me behind her staring down my apron as if the pie might make a run for it. When shall I give it to her? After I've helped her into her pelisse? She's already slipping on her gloves. Of course I'll have to keep the napkin, I hope she shan't mind that. The casing's dry enough.

And if she should? If she should mind? How do I give a lady a meat pie on a doorstep? Do I say, here, Miss, I happen to have a pie in my pocket? Or, I know you're hungry, believe me Miss, anyone who looks at you will know. Your voice alone gave it away while you entertained the ladies with your sewing, your respectable establishment and your sagging gown. And Nancy about to heave two tins of decent food over to the church like slop buckets.

"Thank you," she says. For an instant she looks straight into my eyes. Have I been staring? I opened the door and didn't know I'd done it. I drop a curtsey and she starts down the steps. I watch her make her way past the railings, and it seems to me that her boots barely touch the ground, as if she was light enough for the stinging breeze to carry her.

Something happens to me then. I climb out of myself, pushing my chest open from the inside like the double doors in the drawing room. In truth I feel my feet strike the pavement, the pie dragging down my apron like a stone. I see myself catch up with her beyond the hedge that rings the square. .

I hear the click, click and scrape of the area door below me. "You all right up there, Sal?" There is a clatter of tins and I know without looking that Nancy's holding both with one hand and pulling the door shut with the other. I take the pie out of my pocket: it sits golden and perfect in its nest of crumpled linen, and I could dash it on the steps. I break it neatly in halves.

"Have a piece of this, Nan." I pass it to her in the napkin.

"Don't mind if I do," she chuckles. "You're a sly one, you are.

DAISY BEHAGG

The Opposite of Dave

I liked you because you were the opposite of Dave.
You never told me what you'd benched
that week, the latest banter from the lads,

or talked me through the method
of your protein-shake regime,
before telling me how poetry was stupid.

You listened so hard you barely spoke.
You never even joined the gym.
In bed, there were no hackneyed

pornographic expectations. My body
was something sacred, barely to be touched,
much less owned. You held me gently, hands soft

as the smoothed inside of a girl's ring –
unblemished, white as talc –
even with my legs around you, my whole form pliant

to your touch, it never crossed your mind
to take advantage,
or even take your t-shirt off.

When I told you it was over, you understood –
we'd be together one day, when I'd grown up,
when I could love myself, as you did.

You weren't angry.
You were the opposite of Dave,
and I want you to know that when Dave called

to say he missed me, I said:
What are you doing
right now?

MARY WOODWARD

The Sellotape Factory

You said we were moving to the countryside
where there'd be fresh air and green fields.
And there were. Just not very near us, not near

where we now lived in a new beige brick house.
What we did get was a length of churned up
clay, and a wire fence at the end looking onto

the Sellotape factory. At least it's a clean new
factory, you said at first, meaning well, it's not
the old blackened kind with evil smoking

chimney stacks. Like most post-war factories
it worked twenty four hours a day - less factory
than chemical plant, so what was to have been

our fresh air was laced with the petrolly smell
of glue. On fine days we'd stand at the fence
and weave our fingers in the diamond hatch

of the springy wire, pushing our faces into it
till we were stencilled. Nice men in overalls
would bowl over to us rolls of Sellotape,

the ones that were not quite round enough or
too lumpy to be packaged up for the lorries.
No, we didn't mind the factory. It was you who

turned against it, who couldn't sleep because
of the mechanical hum at night, who took to
writing to the local paper and calling meetings.

Not that anyone else much cared. You were the
only ones who'd believed in the green fields and
the fresh air, the ones who had been conned.

STEPHEN SANTUS

In a Restaurant

This gesture I make to ask for the bill,
Writing on the air
With an imaginary ballpoint,
I learnt from Christopher,
Who learnt it from his father,
Who learnt it himself somewhere.

Christopher's father is long dead:
He echoes less and less.
How strange that what survives of us
Is what we would hardly guess.

VIRGINIA ASTLEY

How did I ever think this would be ok?

Here we all are at the wedding party,
your sister has married my ex,
the one I left for you,
this winter's afternoon they married,
in that same riverside church, your sister
pale and gorgeous, Russell in his kilt.
His mother and his sisters are here,
downing rum punch in the lounge.
They seem to avoid me, possibly
because I was the one who slung
his bass guitar into the Thames.
That was before you and I were,
before London and Liverpool,
before Oxford and Monmouthshire.
But the last time I was in this house,
I can hardly speak, the last time,
was the day we buried you.
And I remember your father,
who had never bought your CDs,
breaking down in Tower Records.
And that day, your poor body,
the only thing the same, your hands.

RICHARD BERENGARTEN

Rimbaud

Precocious pupil, teenage layabout,
he's played provincial brat, brash schoolboy slut,
barbarian beast, filthy louse-ridden mutt –
until piss-artist drink-mates chuck him out;
absinthe and argot mingling in his throat,
teacher's best pet, deranged, turns foul-slanged slob,
illumination-seeker, cannon-gob,
working his passage on a drunken boat . . .
And then he's twenty-two. And poetry stops.
And then, as if he's cleaned up, done the cure,
and doesn't need the hit, crack, high (or crutch?),
his previous life, he says, has been *rinçures* –
rinsewater, dishswirl, drainwaste, sloshmurk, slops –
yeah, been there, done that, thank you very much.

LISA BROCKWELL

The Veranda

Goodbye! Look, the visitors are leaving.
In the rear view mirror they see a woman
and her child waving. The veranda is old
and has felt the weight of other women,
children, dogs, boots. They see a picture
of harmony, mother and child, all is right
with the world. The air is cool inside
the car, the child has smoothed the woman,
they agree, then turn to debate
which restaurant they'll try tonight.

Long ago, as a student, I supervised
at a children's holiday camp. It was as arid
and dull as standing for a week in a sandstorm,
skin stinging and nowhere to go. Hours
staring into space, games evenings and endless
trips to the beach en masse in buses. Milk
and vinegar, that combination of boredom
and vigilance, unable to look away
because she might drown or he might wander
but thirsting for the privacy of a book.

She would like to step off the veranda
to unstrap her shoes and thoughts in the grass
but the boy wants to ride his bike off the edge
and the woman must be the brake, the fence.
She invents a better game, less about
being a crazed playboy in a speedboat,
more about the thrumming jiggle and thrill
riding over the bumps where the planks join.
The visitors have gone and the house
beckons; they stay on the veranda, for now.

JULIAN BROUGHTON

Vegetable Patch

When she with her decisiveness
one morning died, her voice lived on.

He heard it – heard her – urging him
to tell next door *You keep those damn' kids*

quiet; to dust the mantelpiece;
to cancel half the daily milk.

And yes, he'd check the doors were locked,
damp down the fire, wash before bed.

But six months on, she gave no hint
of what to do with all those carrots.

Store in a cool dry place? With soil
adhering still, or scrubbed and clean?

He'd leave them, for the moment, in the shed.
Take off those grubby boots was all she said.

JENNY DANES

On my Grandmother's Bench

It's in the summer, mostly,
when we step through the
conservatory's heavy air
to perch on the patio's bench:
dusty wood, aged with
lichen blooms, tired cracks,
a limp in one leg.
She is always on my left,
having shuffled to the far side,
cautious but straight backed,
over the tilting paving slab
that she warns me to avoid.
I look sideways at her hands
folded in her lap; sometimes
I take one, gentle with its
slack flesh and resting vines,
greasy from the copious
rainbow sheen of sun cream,
and she'll smile and pat me
clumsily. Here we sit, clasping gently,
matching gazes onto rosebushes and
birdfeeders, and she nods while
I let my worries creep into the warm air.

SALLIE DURHAM

I Left My Hair in San Francisco

You want haircut? Long pretty hair, nice.
Twenty two dollar I tidy-up, yes, thirty
dollar for you, I wash hair please, you sit
here. Where is parting? Where you from?
You live London? London nice. Queen
nice lady. I cut here? I take this much.
I go *snipsnip*, I make you nice pretty hair
for holiday. You love jewellery? Nice
jewellery next street, pink store, you
buy something pretty, ok? I go *chopchop*,
nice bob, look pretty. You want me cut
bangs? You want see eyebrow? I cut bangs
straight across. I go *hackhack*, look nice,
look ten year younger. You have child?
Why you no have little boy, brother for girl,
play together, nice, you want me dry hair
straight or curly? I dry curly, look nice,
won't see *hackhack* when curl under.
I take dollar for tidy-up, look rubbish,
I take dollar, I spoil holiday with bad haircut,
I go *hackhack*, I give you terrible theatre wig,
I turn you into Richard the Third, I make you
cringe at reflection, I make you wish you not
come in, I make you wish you walk past window,
past tattoo boss-man rolling bad cigarette,
past my dirty scissors going *snipsnip chopchop
hackhack* –
I make you wish you keep walking, not stop,
keep long pretty hair for holiday.

EMILY GOLDMAN

Vigil

in los angeles
on the ground floor of the hospital
giant wax doctors pace the halls and write with invisible ink.
they are actors in a television show.
upstairs, my brother dies.

i haven't slept in three days
sitting at the bedside
staring at the throat
waiting for the last breath
which i do not see
because i have gone in search of a salad.

i race towards the elevators
and before me is a wall of young men
my brother's age
holding clipboards.
"stop," they say. "you were in the shot
and you've got to sign a release form."

i sign the form.
everyone is released.
my brother dies as Woman with Salad crosses in front of the camera.

in the room upstairs
he looks like a mannequin
monstrous and translucent
and through the window there is nothing
but a perfect glaze of sky.

DOREEN GURREY

Vocab.

Jock Ellis loved words; irregular verbs,
plurals; *'antenna, anybody?*
What about louse?'

He taught us sentence corrections, spelling, vocabulary
colonising our books with neat columns of ticks
all their tails tucked in.

Collective nouns were up on the wall: a shrewdness of apes,
a coalition of cheetahs, a marvel of unicorns.
'The female swan is called a pen;
you should also know these: filly, mare, vixen, bitch.

Now, three synonyms for lazy. I wrote *indolent, apathetic*
and for good measure, *indifferent*

so that when Miss Pyecock the games teacher
crowed *'run you lazy goose,'* I hissed out my newly hatched words.

Later, I picked up my pen and wrote
tyrant, despot, martinet, feeling my swan's neck
stretch, elongate, grow.

LORN MACINTYRE

Satori

My grandfather didn't know he was a Taoist.
He had fished the river Awe for sixty years.
Life is sensed as a flowing movement,
a power like wind or water. When he cast,
it was the bank that moved, not the river.
The osprey with the salmon in its talons
needed no metaphor to describe its beauty.
He saw the suchness of the landscape,
the great whole, perfect, sky, mountain,
as in a painting by the Zen K'un-t'an.
There is no Gaelic for the term *satori*,
the solution lying beyond the intellect,
that flash of delighted intuition, sensing
that a salmon is lying in the current,
while not seeing a ripple with the eye.
If I had told him: 'you read the river
like a book, noting between the lines
what other fishermen fail to spy,'
he would have clouted me on the head,
the way Zen Masters took the big stick
to pupils who insisted on comparison.
The river needs no language, no homage.
It goes its on way, like the osprey
which will never run out of sky.

SHIRLEY WAITE

Unravelling

The pinking shears lived
On their own special shelf in the cupboard;
Shiny black handles, rows of silver teeth,
Too heavy to lift. My mother could –
She could do anything when I was young.
Nights, weekends, her second job, cash in hand –
Singer, material, blue tailor's chalk,
Tissue paper patterns, hedgehog of pins.
Then the shears: high priestess makes the first cut,
Blades grinding, shark-like, slicing through fabric.
A pile of soft shapes falls like a jigsaw,
Stitched into wedding dress, blouse, winter coat.

They still sleep on a shelf in the cupboard
And she likes to stroke the worn enamel,
Though they are too heavy for her to lift
And she doesn't know what to call them
Or what they do.

MANUS McMANUS

Peru

It was given to Tommy Synnott to tell me how she had stepped into the traffic on the coast road, been struck by a car and killed. He hadn't seen it happen, but he knew that she was dead: he could tell from the stain on the road. As he stood on the other side of the front-garden wall, I searched his face for signs of deception, but there was nothing watchful in his gaze. There was even some spittle at the corners of his mouth.

Other evidence followed, of course. Earlier that afternoon, I had seen Mr McBride leaving his house in the company of my uncle and a garda; and the accident was reported on the five o'clock news. My aunt, whose eyes were red from weeping, had begun to prepare food for the McBrides' relatives, who, she said, would be coming up from the country. Mrs Lynch dropped in to discuss the event. She drank a large brandy and, from time to time, pressed a folded handkerchief to the corners of her eyes.

I left them and ran out into the garden to search for a sign. Clouds lay along the edges of the sky, but overhead the evening was clear. I heard a football being kicked, and saw it rise above some hedges farther down the street; a pair of seagulls flew away in the direction of the shore; a crow changed position on the ribs of our television aerial. Everything was perfectly normal, but my heart was racing.

I ran down by the rose-beds, checking the flowers for greenfly. I opened some snapdragons and peered inside. I ran my fingers over the moss that lined the cracks in the garden path, and lifted a stone from the rockery to look at the millipedes and greybacks scuttling for cover. There was nothing out of place.

At the end of the garden I stood under the trees and watched the shadow of the house as it advanced over the lawn. The Angelus rang across from St Gabriel's, and a sudden gust of wind disturbed the trees above me. I looked up and saw a chestnut falling through the branches. It bounced off the lower boughs and dropped at my feet. I picked it up and split the shell; but instead of finding a bonbon or a mothball, or a blue eye, I saw an ordinary brown nut. I set it on a tree stump and smashed it with a rock, but all that came out was a pale green pulp.

I turned and made my way back down the garden. The sound of a referee's whistle came faintly from the playing fields at St Anne's, and the smell of burning weeds hung in the air. I watched bitterly as a pair of swallows dipped and banked above the hedges.

Returning to the kitchen, I sat at the table and tried to stay calm by playing draughts against myself. Mrs Lynch had left, and my aunt was peeling apples. My uncle came back from the hospital. I heard his keys jangling in the pocket of his coat as he draped it over the banisters. When he came into the kitchen, he went to my aunt and stood beside her with his head bowed. He lifted an apple from the counter and turned it in his fingers. Speaking softly, he said that he had dropped Mr McBride back home and left him alone at his request. He wasn't sure he had done the right thing, because Mr McBride was in shock. He lowered his voice further, but I heard the words 'skull' and 'rupture'. He brought the apple to his mouth, but he did not bite it.

I had the feeling that something enormous was growing in the shadows of this September evening. I was used to the lies that my uncle – and everybody else – had been engaged to tell me. They often referred to a world that had existed before my 'birth', a world that, apparently, would go on after my 'death'. That kind of talk was an everyday thing, but there was something sinister in this new story of theirs. What it was I couldn't quite tell, because, of course, nothing had happened as they described it. Mrs McBride wasn't dead – there wasn't as much as a scratch on her. I knew what had happened: just before daybreak, a long black car had turned down our street and pulled up outside her house. She had been expecting it and, so, with her high-heel shoes in her hands, she had run down the driveway and climbed in. Then she had been driven away under the sleeping windows of our street.

I had discovered her only the previous June. Her husband had brought her up from Cork, where they had been married, to live in the house next to ours. She was tall, with blonde hair, and eyes that were green like rose leaves. Her lips seemed redder than other people's, even though she wore no lipstick, and when she smiled you could see that she was gentle and kind.

I fell in love immediately, and persuaded my aunt that I should be the one to bring the tea tray into the drawing room whenever Mrs McBride paid us a visit. I used to look in on them occasionally, and, when it was time, remove the tray under their approving glances. Back in the kitchen,

I would take the spoon from Mrs McBride's half-finished strawberries and cream, and, having examined the tracks left on the spoon by her lips, place it in my mouth. After a few weeks of this, sensing something unrequited, I took to kissing the spoon before sliding it in among her strawberries. I once had to correct my aunt when she tried to take the bowl I had prepared for Mrs McBride. I had no idea what Mrs McBride knew of all this, but it seemed to me then that things were just beginning. Now, I knew only that she had been taken away from me, and I detected in the details of the accident – the injuries to her head, the ruptured organs, the stain on the road – a certain malice.

My uncle came over to the table. He rested a hand on my shoulder and looked solemnly at the draughtsmen. It seemed for a moment as if he was about to speak, but he just squeezed my shoulder and left the room. I knew the game: my uncle had been at it long before this latest hoax. For years, he had been taking me to museums and galleries, old churches and decayed places. To give him his due, he never seemed to enjoy his part in the deception; I often saw a faraway look in his eye as he concluded a lecture on some monument or relic. Nevertheless, one day, standing above a glass case containing the bones of a Viking invader, my uncle wondered aloud if he might not have been slain by Brian Boru himself. He stood there for a while as if considering the merit of the idea, but I saw in his delay an invitation to develop an abiding fear of death.

He read aloud from typewritten notes that had been pinned next to a medieval half-jaw, and he told me that he pitied the people of the age as they must have suffered terribly from rotting teeth and primitive methods of extraction. He tried to engage me in a conversation about the eras that he felt might have been most hospitable to 'two modern fellows like ourselves', but I would not be drawn. So, he led me into another part of the museum and told me how I might never have been born.

Early in the century, he said, there was a brief period of heroism in our country in which my grandfather had played a part. As we wandered among displays of revolvers and rusty bayonets, bloodstained jackets and bullet-pierced hats, he told me how my grandfather, standing on one side of a hole in the wall of a building in Abbey Street, had exchanged grenades with a British soldier who had been standing on the other. Fortunately, my grandfather had been able to toss the soldier's grenade back through the breach – 'casually', his comrades had reported. Without this moment of courage, he might never have survived to father the child who was to become my mother.

I could not tell exactly what my uncle made of my tears. He agreed to take me home, but he drove by way of Abbey Street, where he slowed almost to walking speed and peered up at the buildings on either side of us. He took care also to point out the O'Connell Monument, the Custom House, and the North Strand, where, he said, German bombs had fallen in 1941.

History books began to appear around the house, and my uncle opened a subscription to *National Geographic*. I was encouraged to read the newspaper each evening, and, occasionally, invited to stay up to watch some documentary that had been prescribed for me – one that usually involved dead soldiers or doomed expeditions. At the end of these programmes, my uncle, looking at his watch and seeing that it was past my bedtime, would sigh and say, 'All good things come to an end.'

My aunt crossed the room to switch on the light. For a few moments, as I watched her return to the counter and pick up her knife, I was afraid; but I reminded myself that the haunted look in her face was premeditated and part of the general deception. I knew that the people on our street were going about their business as usual – peeling potatoes, filling coal scuttles, reading the late editions – and that their movements would be measured and proper, their faces sober and reflective, giving nothing away. I knew that my uncle would be in Connolly's bar, rehearsing a speech he would deliver to me later – perhaps from the top of the stairs, looking out the landing window towards the McBrides' house. And, of course, there would be a funeral, people weeping over an empty coffin, and Mr McBride inconsolable at the grave. But it wouldn't work, no matter how they acted: it was all a fake.

This had become clear to me during the previous Christmas holidays. My uncle had been guiding me around the rooms of the National Gallery, and we halted at a large painting of a group of gleaners in a French wheat-field. They stooped in the warm evening light, searching for grain among the stubble. As my eyes roamed the picture, I was startled to see, in the lower right-hand corner, a boy with my face. The artist had not been able to help himself; he had set me in the painting just as someone might inadvertently reveal the answer to a riddle. After a brief shock, I decided that it was no more strange to see myself in a painting than to see my name in another's hand; but I noticed that the artist had put me in winter clothes, while everyone else was dressed for warm weather. In the distance, a church rose above a line of trees, and two windows on its spire looked back at me like a pair of eyes.

We walked back through the chilly streets to where my uncle had parked the car. Christmas lights hung above our heads; beyond them, in a clear winter sky, was a full moon. When I looked up, I felt a dizzy sensation in my stomach, so I lowered my eyes to the shop windows.

We passed a boutique in which a mannequin pointed a finger over the passing traffic to a tropical beach on a poster in a travel agent's window: a bather, waist-deep in turquoise water, held up a speared fish. The arrows of her trident pointed down the street to a window festooned with heraldic flags. Among the standards with their chevrons and dragons and blue-tongued lions, a solitary knight stared out through his visor. I followed his gaze across the street to a window full of television sets. I dragged my uncle over to look at them. On one screen a pirate ship broadsided a frigate; on another, a footballer scored a goal; elsewhere, tanks rolled across a desert, and two doctors discussed a fever chart.

I followed my uncle down the pavement to where he stood looking at some mannequins dressed in winter coats. My eye was drawn to a large silver ball resting at their feet. In it I could see reflected the red and green of the coats, the white Christmas lights strung between the buildings, the full moon beyond them and, in the centre, my own face.

Overwhelmed by the boundlessness of it all, aware for the first time of God's plan, and knowing that news of my least action was awaited by surgeons, judges, astronomers, duellists, wedding parties, firing squads, leper colonies, and football teams in the middle of their matches, I fell to the ground. Though I was smiling, a look of horror crossed my uncle's face.

He lifted me from the pavement and took me to Bewley's for a cup of tea. I sat at a corner table, holding a glass of water that he had begged of a waitress on our arrival, and I watched the customers coming and going, shoppers and well-wishers, people reading newspapers or writing Christmas cards. Two nuns sat at the table next to ours, but they did not respond to my knowing looks. My uncle returned with beans on toast and tea for two. He tried to reassure me by behaving normally: as always, he mashed his beans into a paste and flipped one half of the toast onto the other to make a sandwich, and he turned his cup after setting it down, in order to hide the crumbs on the inside of the rim. While he ate his meal and told me how he had once fainted at a football match, I felt the dizziness returning. I wondered where all these people went when I was not around, what possible other purpose they could serve. As I looked along the counter at the machines – meat-slicers, grills, steamers and ovens – I felt a sickness rising in my stomach, and, holding my hand over my left eye, which was causing me great pain, I threw up on the floor.

Afterwards, I realised that the nuns' indifference had been perfectly in order, as had my uncle's lengthy apologies and the pale face of the waitress. My aunt put me to bed and sent for the doctor. He diagnosed flu, and prescribed three days' rest.

My aunt brought me an atlas and some books on history, which she said might 'perk me up'. I knew immediately, of course, that they were meant to increase my fear; by reading these books, I was supposed to discover the age and size of the universe. There were drawings of dinosaurs and mastodons; photographs of coronations and bombed-out cities; charts of the routes taken by explorers; diagrams of the orbits of planets and the circulation of the blood. I lay back on the pillows, listened to the rain passing over the rooftops and nursed my scepticism. These books... how was I supposed to take them seriously? I knew that the one in my hand had not been printed on a press; it had been formed whole and brought directly to my bed. And I realized that when I looked at pictures of the ruins of Ancient Greece, at fallen pillars and collapsed corridors, it made no difference whether this or that pillar fell in this or that direction. I knew that it made no difference whether or not the ruins themselves existed, and that for His purpose only the pictures were necessary.

Sometimes my aunt would chair a quiz at the dinner table. 'What's the capital of Peru?' she might ask, or 'What's the biggest lake in the world?' or 'Which planet is farthest from the sun?' Though I understood that this was her duty, and obliged her with some answer or other, I was disappointed by her enthusiasm. What I knew was that Peru was white at its centre and purple around its edges. It was an inch wide and two inches long. It was bordered by pink Ecuador, yellow Colombia, green Brazil, pink Bolivia and yellow Chile. There was no such place as Peru, yet I realized that, were I to set out to find it, God would set it in my path. That was the way the world was made.

As I sat at the table, sliding the pieces across the red and black squares, my aunt rolled out some pastry for an apple tart. Occasionally, she lifted a hand to wipe away a tear, but she did not speak. Silently, I cursed her tears. I cursed my uncle's diffidence, and I cursed Tommy Synnott for the spittle on his mouth. They frightened me, like all the others, yet somehow they seemed more cruel.

I felt that I should declare my knowledge. A voice was shouting in my head, but all it said was 'Haagghhh!' I ran my thumbs into my temples. I knew that in order to discover more I should have to say to my aunt, 'You can stop now. I know all about it: it's some kind of test. It's all made up... Mrs McBride isn't dead... nobody dies. God has told you all to act this way. You know I'll find out in the end – when I'm supposed to die and I don't – so you might as well stop now.'

Then she would say, 'Yes, yes, you're right. I'm sorry, but we had to do it this way. It was His will. All of this was for you. You are the reason for all the things that fill the world — gardens, swallows, September evenings; wardrobes, sharks and locomotives; shop signs, flags, aerials, maps, Vikings, empty crisp-bags on the pavements, the coins in your pocket. You are the reason for everyone on this street, and everything about them. These things are just part of the plan.' She would flip the pages of her cookery book. 'Why, even this book, the words on the pages, and the order of the pages... all for you.'

And then Mrs McBride would come through the door – dressed in white and smiling like an angel – and she would continue the explanation: 'See? Road accidents . . . not real. Bomb-blasts and massacres, famines and air-disasters . . . all made up. Why, the passengers on those flights are aware of their fate. In fact they find it tedious. They have been in every air disaster you've ever heard of. It has been their job ever since you were put into the world. It is the same for victims of shootings and stabbings and drownings, and for suicides and for the people in the cancer wards.' She would smile, and say, 'We are angels. We do not die. We are not buried.'

My aunt would step towards me, and say, 'I am not your aunt, and your uncle is not your uncle. There are no aunts or uncles, no fathers or mothers. So your parents did not die. No one died. No one has ever died.'

Then she would leave the kitchen, and Mrs McBride would follow, beckoning with movements of her slender hands. They would join all the people who, their duties discharged, would be leaving their houses for the last time. I would rise slowly from my chair, and I would move through the doorway and down the hall and out into the street to watch the neighbours parading past on their way to the shore where everyone would be transfigured and raised into the clouds... And then, turning, I would see the tall figure that had for years eluded me. Wearing the red and white robes foretold in the churches and galleries, the light around Him so brilliant that I should hardly see His face, He would step towards me, soundlessly.

My aunt went to the sink and rinsed flour from her hands. I looked at her in disbelief. Why did she torture me this way? How could she, after all that had happened? Why would she not break from the others? My heart was pounding. Still with her back to me, she said, 'Who's winning?'

I said nothing, and brought my hands to my lap.

She turned from the sink and looked at me, but I could not meet her gaze.

'I know you're sad,' she said. 'We all are. But we must be strong. She's with God now. God loves her very much. He loves us all.'

I looked into her eyes then, and I saw that she would not relent, that she would usher me through the days to the funeral, take me for a haircut, buy me a new shirt and tie, and talk to me about heaven.

'Listen,' she said, 'why don't you pop down to the end of the garden and get me a few apples, will you? Don't be long. It looks like rain.'

On my way out I slammed the door. My aunt did not rap on the window, as she would have done on any other day. As I passed by the snapdragons and the rose bushes, as my feet pressed down on the grass and the daisies, as I parted a cloud of gnats, I felt I should weep for them all; they all had been so carelessly created.

Several apples lay in the rough grass as if waiting for me to choose them, but I decided to climb the tree. As I began to pull myself up through the branches, I heard the first drops of rain striking the leaves overhead. Dusk was coming in early and there was a faint orange glow above the coast road. I could see squares and rectangles of amber light appearing along the houses. For a moment, I wondered if I might visit each of those houses, asking people for the truth; but I knew that they all would be unwavering – scraping mutton-fat from dinner plates, drawing curtains, settling into armchairs, filling baths. There was no one, it seemed, who had not been sworn to secrecy.

A gust of damp air pushed through the leaves, and I caught the smell of stale tobacco. I turned on the branch to look down into the next garden, and there I saw Mr McBride, his arms hanging limply by his side, his pipe gone out, his shoes sinking into the clay of a flowerbed. He was staring at the base of a tree trunk. He seemed completely unaware of me, but I knew what he was doing: he was making sure that I saw him so that I would realise how final things were, how strange and lost everybody was, how you could be playing tennis on a bright lawn on a Saturday afternoon, your blonde hair shining in the sun, and by Tuesday be buried under a ton of black earth.

The rain came down harder, and Mr McBride lowered his head. A shadow appeared in the gap between his shirt-collar and his neck. I thought of the raindrops falling into it. His pipe fell from his fingers, and he covered his face with his hands. Then his legs seemed to buckle and he dropped to his knees in the clay.

I heard our kitchen door slam, and my aunt's voice came up the garden impatiently. Mr McBride was weeping into his hands, bowing so low that his forehead was touching the ground. I tried to shout out, but the words stopped in my throat. As I watched my aunt striding up the lawn and signalling for me to come down from the tree, I wondered what it was that God could do that would earn Him my forgiveness.

JENNIFER MILLS

Praise

They speckled fields and highways. Their tiny corpses lay with wings
spread out like cemetery angels. Flocks fell from every sky:
American, African, European, Asian. The mass death of seabirds over the
north Pacific, tens of thousands strong, was thought at first to have
something to do with Fukushima. We only found it when the shoals of
sharks that came to feast on them lit up the radar. Most of the die-offs that
we know about have happened over land, and close to people. The ones I
study began right here.

I open a drawer, take a selection of chest feathers from the box marked
Chest and begin gluing them to the metal. They are fluffy, chick-like, pink
at the tips. On the largest of my monitors, I track the flock as a green flush,
like light cloud on the weather radar, a low pressure system of birds. They
have been circling the area for days. They usually reach the shopping
centre by early evening.

I work for the Institute of Avian Cultural Studies. It sounds grand but
I'm the only one here. The Institute is a bright orange shipping container
sitting in the car park of an empty shopping mall, near the centre of the
concentration. This is a blackspot. Six years ago, right here, five thousand
galahs dropped out of the sky in one afternoon. As you can imagine, the
retail experience suffered. The mall had glass ceilings. The birds cracked
them on impact, terrifying shoppers. You can still see bloodstains, if you
go inside. Some blamed the mall's lights. Some thought it was radiation.
The shopping complex soon closed its doors. But the die-offs kept
coming, and not just here; all over the world, large flocks of birds were
dropping into industrial estates, sheep paddocks, mountain ranges and
suburban streets. The stories went viral, provoking their fair share of
Fortean theories and interactive infographics. The buzz came at just the
right time for Dr Marigold's book. The die-offs have made her career.

At first, the events were studied in isolation. Some flocks were shown
to have botulism from eating dead fish; others may have died of
exhaustion during a long migration. No-one could prove the incidents
were related, that they formed a pattern, although we tried. We made

endless spreadsheets, printed maps and drew connecting lines, but if there was a link, we couldn't see it. So we focused on the local sample, our galahs.

I always loved galahs. They are natural clowns. Play is a strong indicator of intelligence. They used to make me laugh, before the die-offs. Now their approaching *cleat-cleat* chorus gives me shivers.

It was almost by accident that we figured out why our birds were falling. It wasn't botulism or exhaustion. It wasn't radiation, climate change, gas mines, lightning, fireworks or telephone towers. It was praise. After so many years trying to find ways of describing the problem, it was a relief to begin working on something solid. I didn't realise then how much trouble it would bring me, to refashion myself as a manufacturer of priests.

It was Dr Marigold who made the breakthrough. For many years she had been a researcher in bird language and brain science. She had built her career on combining research disciplines, from neuroscience, linguistics, biology and animal behaviour, to approach a description of the birds' social language. She focused on galahs long ago, not because they were dying – at the time the phenomenon was limited – but because they showed intense pair bonding and flock dynamics which approached emergent networks, a describable intelligence. The social dynamic wasn't the exciting part; most of her research was just combining models that other scientists had already described. It was the analogy that brought her all the attention.

I smooth down the chest feathers with a fine brush and replace the box in its drawer. I touch my temples, feel where the wrinkles spread out from the corners of my eyes. My fingers are sticky with glue.

I was Dr Marigold's student when her book came out. Her research assistant through the reviews and the feature articles, head assistant by the time of the TV appearances and unrelenting phone calls. Suddenly we had all kinds of funding and she rewarded my loyalty with a position in the Institute. At thirty-four I'm young to have my own research facility. I'm grateful to her. There is a stack of hardback copies of *Praise: Birds, Ceremony and the Culture of Faith* over by the window. The pink cover looks so joyful, so confident.

I wash my hands at the large stainless steel basin that sits to one side of my work space, leaving the retractable hose in its stand. I wonder if I could use it to improvise a shower. My under-arms are beginning to smell unpleasant. My little lab is filled with fancy equipment, huge screens running custom software, joined parts. Everything is clean except myself. Steel benches, neat shelves, white speakers playing soft piano. Feathers sorted in their boxes. My spare shirt hangs on the hot water pipe. My hands are shaking as I dry them on the small hand towel. I haven't left this room for seventy-four hours. I've slept maybe six of those. Outside, the shopping centre holds a throng of people, the walls of the building spray-painted with slogans. Probably the walls of this container too. It's quiet in here, but I am surrounded.

I don't believe in God, though as an anthropologist I am fully aware that other people need Him. Religiosity is a handy model for under-standing human societies, so why not the societies of birds? I was double-majoring in psychology; I was just filling gaps in my enrolment when I took Dr Marigold's undergrad class in avian intelligence. I'd heard of her, however. We all had. She was a notoriously eccentric figure on campus, the sort of woman who was regarded as at best, impossibly unapproachable and at worst, a sort of villain. Tall, beaky, unmarried and childless, she attracted theories about autism spectrum and personal disaster. Her home life was a well-kept secret; it was rumoured she slept at her desk. No-one ever saw her laugh, nor did she seem to have any friends on staff. Dr Marigold had been one of several researchers in the 1990s who had argued that parrots had individual names, before the evidence proved it. Working with birds made her an obvious target for student cartoonists, and I got to know her first in caricature: with a parrot on her shoulder, or as the witch fattening Hansel and Gretel in a giant cage, their emaciated bodies weighed down with clumsily grafted wings. In person, she was gruff and clever, and at first I was afraid of her. But then I began to see and value her strangeness for what it was: genius.

When I bother to feel betrayed, those old images come to mind: myself as Gretel, a caged bird. But I am here because I want to be here, and I'm more frustrated than sad. When I feel this way I go to the sink and wash these hands, or my face, or I turn up the music, or pace the twenty-four foot length of this box. I check the bars are locked fast on the side which opens into the car park. I check the boards that cover its two small windows, which thankfully have security grilles on the outside. I check the time, to make sure I keep track of the approaching dusk. I squat to piss in a large specimen jar and pour the urine down the sink. I last went out to use the proper bathroom two nights ago, to find that the cleaner has not been for days. This is no surprise. It's not safe, and there isn't any money left to pay him. There used to be a security guard at the car park entrance. I suppose he must have been let go, unless the protesters have killed him.

Really she was only guessing, going on a hunch, but it turned out to be one of science's great lateral what-ifs. From Dr Marigold's longitudinal studies into bird language had come theories about poetry and song in brain development, the role of proto-art in culture, and then speculation that these large, regular meetings, with their chants and repetitions, might echo some of our own rituals. She never said this to me – I read it in the introduction to her book – but Dr Marigold was raised a Quaker. She claimed to be a rationalist, often told me that science was her religion. I suppose the framework was still there, because it all came out in her writing: the importance of meetings, togetherness, song. It had long been known galahs had at least the intelligence of children. What if there were storyteller figures among them? She followed the thread, and was as surprised as the rest of us when her modelling held up against the evidence. It seemed insane. We thought we knew the limits of consciousness. We thought it was an absurdity to talk about birds as though they had faith.

Analogies are powerful temptations. We impose our own patterns of thought on other species. My ex-flatmate David, a gangly marine biologist who studies octopuses, told me that if cephalopods devised a test for intelligence they would ask how many colours you could project with your skin, what sort of spectrum you could perceive. If there was such a test, humans would fail. By their standards, we're idiots, he said. I wondered what the birds' test would be. What sort of intelligence they mastered. Watching them twist and bicker in the air at cues I couldn't then discern, I thought I could guess. It was not long after I came to work with Dr Marigold that she had her breakthrough, and all her eccentricity and guesswork culminated in a sudden soaring upward, lifting her into the rarer atmosphere of popular science.

I remember the moment when we knew. She had modelled some audio, a hypothetical pattern which might replicate the call and response of the sermon. We had pulled up the sound file and were playing it alongside an old recording. Dr Marigold and I stood transfixed. The troughs and peaks of the sound waves were matching the prediction, and not only visually. When we turned up the volume the two tracks seemed to sing together like a pair of perfectly matched instruments. When my eyes met hers, she actually laughed aloud. It seems small, Dr Marigold and I laughing at a couple of sound waves on a screen, but it was a magnificent feeling. That moment of shared optimism, that sense of making a real discovery, is why I became a scientist in the first place. They say you only get one. I will never have another breakthrough like it. Now I wonder if we knew anything at all.

We didn't call them priests at first. Flock leaders, we called them, vanguard birds, or speech makers – we talked about it as a singular role, though it was a post that many birds took on and abandoned. The ebb and flow of a flock of galahs is really leaderless, emergent. But it made sense to us to talk about the role. Because that was what was changing. The priests were disappearing.

Gradually, these leaders switched register. Their ordinary cries and screeches, full of regular repetitions, parts we had come to recognise as words and phrases, punctuation, and the names of birds, became erratic. They began to exhibit the rhythmic disconnects and dissonances we associate with post-modernist poetry, though of course it's absurd to speak of a postmodern bird. Dr Marigold noticed the pattern shifting,then disappearing, just before the die-offs. It was me who began to refer to these leaders as priests. Priestesses, because most are female. I meant it flippantly, but the idea caught on quickly, like a chant will catch through a crowd.

Perhaps it was a mistake to go to the media first. Her critics flayed Dr Marigold for publishing her findings before she had the data, before she approached any peer-reviewed journals. They called our research pseudo-science. They said that all we had was an analogy, and however useful it was, it wasn't *hard science*. After years of mocking her coldness, people began to call Dr Marigold emotional. But we had solid data, too. We followed up with proper articles, most of which I co-authored. And before we could review our way of describing the behaviour, the religion analogy had already struck a chord with the general public. People were desperate for an answer to the mystery of the die-offs. The media loved it. All the attention made the Dean nervous. He encouraged us to start the Institute. He found the funds and let us use one of the old ornithology labs on campus. I suppose he was trying to pacify his staff.

I thought of the flocks as cults more than anything, and of that cultishness as still a symptom of whatever else was going on environmentally. I suspected they were responding to climate change, but I wouldn't make that claim without evidence. I was very hesitant to use words like ceremony and ritual at first. Even if the religious analogy worked, we were looking at its loss; at a system failure for which religion had no answers. But we couldn't say no to the money from the Christian groups. With those funds we were able to pursue our experiments, so long as we used their terminology. With the money from the chemical companies and the fracking people, keen to support anything that countered theories they might be to blame, I found I could afford to send my designs to high-end robotics experts over in Japan and China. And I had just taken delivery of the latest of these models, the grey, parrot-shaped structure of GALA 9.3, when the protesters found me.

In a break in the music I hear the chants outside and I go to the window. There's a crack between the boards, right above the stack of books. I lean my elbows on them and peer out at the mob. They are very young, these mob members, some just round-faced children. Behind them I can see the blackened, smoking shell of my work car, a compact hybrid which still looks cheery in shape despite its being reduced to a charcoal exoskeleton. The afternoon light is becoming gentle and the spray-rendered wall of the shopping centre looks flushed behind the crowd, like the chest feathers of a galah. There's gold reflected in the windows. The birds will be here soon.

Even now, I refer to GALA 9.3 as the priestess. Using this language is a habit I can't break. Perhaps, if we are right, the birds themselves have a name for the role. But of course, we'd never be capable of pronouncing it. We don't speak their language. We couldn't say we know what's being said in their sermons, or even if the words have any weight, the way that ours do. My friends, when I still met up with them, used to tease me for talking to birds – they'd call me Dr Doolittle, or they'd croak a 'hello-cocky' as they passed me in the hallways – and I always corrected them. I don't talk to the galahs. We can't understand what they are saying. Understanding is too high a bar. We make educated guesses. It's just a matter of recognising what certain patterns *do*. A crude and meaningless grasp of language, but let that be a matter for speculation in the airy attics of philosophers. In the field, meaning can be bypassed altogether. It's function we're after, behavioural change. Perhaps I have had moments of believing that the patterns we're describing, the fit of the analogy, makes it right. I'm past that now. I know the spiritual interpretation is all myth. So if you're going to tease me with storybook names, call me Daedalus.

We weren't in the business of making metaphysical claims, but there were obvious advantages to the support of the Christians, who saw it as their territory. So we moved the Institute off campus and into the field, out here to the mall, to be closer to the action and further from the Dean. Dr

Marigold didn't feel hijacked; I do, but who can change the system? It's a long time since universities funded independent research, and the church is no different to any other corporation.

After years of struggling through evidence-based research, Dr Marigold was high on theory, spent most of her time touring and giving talks, said anything was worth the ideas having a life. And it was always the ideas she was faithful to. She was answering questions that were supposed to lie outside human understanding, in the gap between our knowledge and the impossible otherness of a bird's mind. What role could religiosity play in social life? Is it essential to group cohesion? Do birds have culture? How complex does language need to be before we can call it prayer? And (more quietly) if these mass bird deaths are a sign of cultural despair, if they are in fact suicides, could there be environmental factors at play? Why are the priests disappearing? Dr Marigold came alive, as if her closed, eccentric manners were just preparation for fame, a chrysalid stage out of which she emerged triumphant and winged. Right now she's off in France, presenting a seminar, while I'm in my container, soldering the joints of a mechanical bird, the doors bolted, the music on. I turn the volume up to drown the chants. Last night they held an all-night candlelight vigil complete with singing. I expect tonight will be the same, unless this works. Meanwhile, me and Beethoven and GALA 9.3 are keeping each other company. I spread her tail feathers, sniff for the scent of real bird which is still held in the fibre. Stroke the feathers back into their perfect, zippered shape.

Last year, before we even had time to predict it, all of the priestesses were gone. No bird flew ahead to take the pulpit. No leader sang the flocks aloft. They simply flew in a leaderless mass: flew into power lines, or into the poison air over smokestacks, and fell to this asphalt graveyard. It is awful to watch, even through the tiny tracking cameras. You don't have to understand the structure of their language to hear the panic in their voices, see their descent as a manifestation of despair. I couldn't keep watching them, but I didn't want to compromise Dr Marigold's work with my interventions. So with her permission I started a project within the Institute, which I jokingly referred to as the 'development wing' – a corner of this room which soon spread and overtook the rest.

I started by playing Dr Marigold's older recordings from the days before the die-offs. At first playing them in the air, via kite and then via remote-controlled plane. Later I tried taking the birds into the lab and playing it to them on these mounted speakers. The birds did not respond well. They repeated certain phrases, battering through the patterns, then fell silent, as if I had told them an awkward joke. Then I began working with edited versions. My own synthesis of their speeches. I was aiming for babble-luck, Thorndike's term for accidental sense. Our critics accuse us of anthropomorphism, but it's the other way around. We've thought of the birds as cheap mimics for so long, and now I am desperate to copy them. I remember a snippet from Irene Pepperberg that was pinned to the cork board in our old lab:

"if an act is performed because the imitator understands its purpose — to reach a goal, be it an object or intentional communication, otherwise impossible to obtain — then the act is intentional, complex, likely indicates cognitive processing..."

It's a *hoc ergo propter hoc* situation; just because the die-offs are happening at the same time as the change, doesn't make it cause and effect. But the chances of it working are too high for that to matter.

I wash my hands again, take a break while the glue sets. I stretch out on the couch, my head propped on a cushion, and stare at the little hatch overhead. My eyes are sore. Out there, the birds will be circling. I try not to worry about doubt. Instead I remind myself of its abstract necessity. Doubt must always be there, the context of all knowledge, like the element in which it lives. Everything we know is a kind of reconciliation with doubt. Nothing is ever proven, only suggested, shown to work. I suppose there is, even in science, an element of faith, however undetectable. Instead of a leap, there is a small step across a grey area. How far do we push the guesses, the fortunate copies, our babble-luck, before we can say that we understand?

I never thought I'd be applying Pepperberg's test to myself. Perhaps I have guessed wrong, and don't understand the purpose of the birds' sermons at all. Perhaps my model is too weak to prove anything. I hold her carefully as I stick the last feathers under her belly. The early priests were clumsy, crude things – there is a prototype on my desk which looks like childish papier mâché strapped to an iPod. The first few were abject failures. Many crashed. Others were brought down by the birds themselves.

My clumsy models were letting the project down. When I read that the French had developed a small ornithopter based on a gull, I wrote for permission to apply their design, worked out a flimsier version of it, and had one made. I started redirecting funds from the Institute's research wing. Thought I'd cover my tracks before Dr Marigold returned. I tested it with old recordings first, and got the same responses as before. The birds sat and muttered, picked at their chests. Group by group, I watched them plummet into the car park around me. It was as if they were mocking me. I stood helpless at my hatch, in the bright and awful rain.

These feathers have been gathered from previous events. Though they live mainly on a diet of fruit and bark, the pink parrots are not averse to killing when they have to. The scent of their own discarded feathers helps convince them the robot belongs. Over time the designs have acquired more complexity, though still none has succeeded. I mute Beethoven with a tap of my finger and open the sound editor.

I run through the sermon. Its trills and screeches, cleats and repeats are familiar to me now as though I could actually understand them, but it's the way I might believe I understand a love song in another language. Maybe the birds make music and not language. Maybe it's pure emotion. I save the track to the chip and back it up on the cloud. Then I take the chip out with tweezers – it is as tiny and fragile as a bird's rib – and carry it back to my work bench.

Failure is an important teacher. The project is much more sophisticated now. My synthetic tracks are having more of an effect. The last group really listened. And the local wedge-tailed eagles and feral cats have cleaned up most of the mess. I push the chip into its slot and close the little metal compartment. The priestess is complete. Her sermon is ready to fly. I place the tweezers back on the bench and hook my fingers under its cold edge as I breathe.

I didn't really care when the university sent us away. So much of what they do is public relations now. I didn't want to be called a pseudo-scientist; I knew our research was solid. But when the Christians turned on us too, I began to feel that what we were doing was not just radical, but dangerous. Dr Marigold had a couple of death threats early on, but they stopped, or she stopped telling me about them. I should have seen this protest coming.

The Christians don't like the research anymore. They don't like the Institute, particularly my wing. They say if we can manufacture the faith of birds then we might work on people next. They write op eds about mind control. Personally I can see how this fictional research would be useful to them, but they argue that God won't like it. They can't prove He exists, but they have lists of what He doesn't like. It is ridiculous, because what we have learned here applies only to these specific parrots. It wouldn't even work on another group of galahs; their languages are local and we are only working with this dialect. It certainly wouldn't work on a crow, or a sparrow, or an eagle, let alone a person. I think they are afraid they will be out of a job. Afraid that we might replace their faith with a series of algorithms, or patterns, and reveal to their flocks how crude their shepherding has always been. As if they have a patent out on mystery.

It's started a schism of sorts, with the various churches trying to bite each other off like limbs, and in the midst of that, I am allegedly playing God. Or Satan, depending on which of the protesters you listen to. Anyway my funding's finished. The fracking people don't want to offend the Christians, and the university won't do anything without both. The Dean won't even return my calls any more.

In a way, I envy them their faith. I want to believe it too. I want to believe the die-offs are a problem we can solve. I want science to do its job in the world, not just tour around Europe speculating. I believe in this work. I want to believe that all our knowledge can't be reduced to the presence or absence of faith.

I have had to borrow heavily from my personal accounts, and now my credit has run out. I haven't mentioned this to Dr Marigold. But if I can get this to work, our donors might be back. More importantly, the birds might be saved. And then Dr Marigold will return a hero. I lift GALA 9.3 in my hands, extend her metacarpal bones, bones of hollowed steel made halfway across the world. I have tested the beat of her wings, composed every phoneme she will utter. Her words, if I can call them that. I put her down on the bench and tap my screen to turn off the music. The chanting swells up around me in waves. I can hear it through the metal wall. Abomination. Violation. Judgement. Hell. Without the music, it is easier to make out the words.

A few weeks ago in Germany, at an important linguists' conference, Dr Marigold spoke out against my 'renegade theories' and distanced herself from the Institute entirely. She had the good grace to send me an email afterwards, apologising and calling this a 'necessary expedient' and a 'temporary measure.' 'Upon my return we will look again at the state of play and re-assess your role,' the email said. She knows that what I am working on could be her next big break. But she has to be the public face of the Institute. Since then, I have been on my own, and if I do not get this to work, it will be the end for more than birds. I drag the stepladder across to the roof hatch and prop it open. Outside, the voices swell. The crowd has grown.

I check my radar. The flock is gathering. They are so near that I can hear them, their high *cleat-cleat* rising over the chanting. The wind is in my favour. It has to be now. When I set the bird out, I smell smoke. The crowds have easily doubled in size. They have seen the hatch open, are aiming prayers and perhaps rifles at the top of my head. There is a violence in the air which seems leaderless. I can't see them when I stand on my toes, but I can see the tops of their placards, the orange firelight swelling in the shopping mall's windows, and when I look up I see the birds are circling overhead, as if drawn to the frenzy. Chants of anger soar and fade. The screeches of parrots melt into the words. I am evil, I hear, my heart bursting with blood. The birds fly close to us, into the smoke. My model teeters on the tin roof, and I reach my hands through the hatch to raise her wings.

JOHN MURPHY

Jotunheim

In the week he learned that his father was dying, Naoise was punched in the face for the first time in his life. Three boys ambushed him on Camden Street not far from where he lived. The boys took his swatch and fifty pence, and just as he thought it was all over, one of them had punched him in the face for no reason at all. Afterwards, he couldn't remember much of what they had said to him when they were jostling him – that was all mixed up now – but he remembered their names: Pelvis, Rude-boy, and Bandit. Walking the rest of the way home, Naoise replayed the incident over in his mind. He tried to think of something else, but he couldn't. He couldn't help wondering what it would be like to punch someone in the face.

The house he lived in was on a Victorian terrace, but unlike the neighbour's houses it was stylish and modern on the inside. Naoise's father was an architect. His mother had been an architect, too. She met Naoise's father when they were working in a practice on Water Street in New York. She and her girlfriend, a woman called Isobel, wanted a baby. After some initial reluctance Naoise's father had agreed to help them.

"Our baby will have tall genes," Isobel had said.

Six months after Naoise was born, his mother and Isobel were killed when their Taurus was driven off the embankment on the Merritt Parkway by a drunk driver, a currency trader who had just been fired from his job. They were traveling to Westport to sign contracts for the new house they had bought. At the time of the accident, Naoise's father was walking in the Little Flower playground, carrying him in a sling, watching some kids shooting hoops. After the funerals, he resigned from his job, and moved back to Dublin with Naoise. He set up his practice on Merrion Square, and from then on he organised his life around Naoise.

Naoise let himself in and put his school bag down on the hall table. Nemo's tunic was not on the coat stand, he was at the hospital where he worked as a nurse. He was Naoise's father's friend, and had moved in with them the year before. Mrs Blennerhasset came in every day and did most of the cooking and housekeeping, but it was Nemo who changed the sheets on his father's bed. Nemo was very strong. Every day he lifted Naoise's father out of his bed and laid him on the chaise longue under the window while he made up the bed with fresh linen. Not long after he first became ill, his father met Nemo at a hospital fundraiser. He was gentle and easy going, calm like his father. When Naoise first met him three years before, when he was ten years old, he had asked him about his name. "Are you called after the man in the submarine?" Naoise had said, to the amusement of his father.

Naoise put his keys in the table drawer, and went into the downstairs bathroom and washed his face and hands. From the kitchen he could hear Mrs Blennerhasset singing to herself over the radio – a Duran Duran song. He combed his hair forwards and tried to cover up the bruise, and then he went out to the hall and up the stairs.

"Have you got a minute, shorty?" Bandit had said.

The bedroom was dark when Naoise went in, the gazelle-patterned drapes pulled. The light, even in daytime, hurt his father's eyes. Tiny spinnerets of light hovered over the crystal water pitcher on the bedside table. There was a smell of citrus in the room. When he heard the footsteps on the polished oak floor, his father turned his head and said, "Is that you, big fellow?"

"Yes, it's me."

Naoise was the smallest boy in his year at St. Sebastien's. His father was a very tall man, six feet eight inches when he was standing, which was hardly ever nowadays.

"Torus," his father said, taking Naoise's hand.

"Ovolo," Naoise answered, playing the word game his father liked to play.

"Cyma reversa."

"Cyma recta."

When his father was still able to drive, and they were going to the West to the house they had in Leenane, or into town to the Italian restaurant on Capel Street they liked, they would play this game. Naoise was familiar with many of the strange words his father had used in his professional life. *Architrave. Tympanum. Pediment.* Mr Pettigrew, the latin teacher, had been impressed by his knowledge of ancient architecture.

"Bolection," his father said.

After a few moments, when Naoise had failed to answer, not wanting to tire him out, his father said hoarsely, "Water. A glass of water."

He was breathing with difficulty, exhausted by the slight effort of their conversation, a white rime tiding his lips. The glass of water Nemo had

112

filled earlier was still on the table. Naoise put his hand behind his father's head, and brought the glass to his lips. When his father had enough, he raised his hand. Naoise sat on the bed, and rubbed the back of his father's cold, boney wrist. He thought about the word he was going to say in the game. It was an effort not to speak it aloud. He tried to think about something else. He ran his hand along his lapel, down the front of his blazer.

"Let's open you up, Shorty. What have we got in these inside pockets?" Pelvis had said, pulling the blazer buttons off, and throwing them on the ground.

When his father was asleep Naoise walked to the door, and looking back he saw that his father's slippers were crossed over each other under the bed. He tip-toed back again, and knelt down beside the bed. He uncrossed the slippers, and stood up.

"Astragal." he said to himself, and walked out of the room.

The following day, when he came home from school, Naoise walked directly to the kitchen where he found Mrs Blennerhasset ladling stew into a bowl for a girl who was perhaps his own age or a little older. The girl's hair was dyed black and cut in heavy uneven layers. Her eye make up made her look slightly oriental, and her skin was the palest he had ever seen, paler even than his father's. When Mrs Blennerhasset saw Naoise at the door, she pulled out a chair and said:

"This is Eva, my niece. She is staying with me for a while."

Eva nodded to him, and without taking her eyes from him, blew on her spoon. Naoise said hello, and sat down on the other side of the table. Mrs Blennerhasset placed a bowl in front of him and filled it with stew. Since his father had been ill, Naoise had eaten all of his meals in the kitchen, sometimes with Nemo if he wasn't on the night shift, but mostly he ate on his own.

As they ate, watching each other slyly under their fringes, Naoise thought she looked like the girls in the comics his father had brought home from conference trips to Japan. He found himself involuntarily lifting his spoon to his lips at the exact moment she lifted her spoon to her lips.

"Could you please not do that?" Eva said.

"What?"

"The spoon thing," she said. And what's with that bump on your head? There. See?" She had reached over with the soup spoon, almost touching his forehead.

"What bump? What are you on about?" Naoise said.

"That big yokemibob on your noggin. It's hardly a birth mark now, is it?" she said, smiling for the first time, pushing back her chair with her black nyloned knee. "Let me guess. You walked into a pole, did you? No? A spotty gift of puberty? Sooner or later it gets to us all."

She laughed, and Naoise saw that she had a slight gap between her front teeth. He laughed, too, and after that it was easy to to talk to her. She said she liked The Cure and the Fall. She asked him what music he liked. He said he liked Duran Duran and Spandau Ballet. "Saps," she said.

"He probably goes to Irish dancing, the nancy," Rude-boy had said. "La la la la la la lala la. Dance nancy! Dance!"

In the living room, Eva opened her school bag and took out an LP and played it on the stereogram.

"Some dinosaur you got here, Buddy," she said.

After a minute, Mrs Blennerhasset shouted out from the kitchen for them to turn the music down.

"Help me push the sofa," Eva said.

Naoise had never danced with a girl – with anyone – before. Now he was dancing to Hex Enduction Hour in his living room with a girl who looked like she might know people who carried switchblades. They played each side of the record twice.

"I bet he's a fucking bender. He probably likes Depeche Mode and the Bronski Beat," Bandit had said.

After Eva had gone home with Mrs Blennerhasset, Naoise danced on his own without any music. He decided he didn't like Spandau Ballet or Duran Duran anymore. While he danced, he wondered if anyone had ever eaten buffalo lips on toast.

The next day, after school, Naoise went into town with Eva. On Henry Street, she bought Naoise a ninety-nine. He bought her liquorice allsorts on Capel Street. In the Rock Shop on Great Strand Street they looked at second-hand electric guitars.

"Where's the blonde telecaster, Tony?" Eva asked a man in a motorcycle jacket.

"Some guy traded an L6 for it," Tony said, pointing to a flat looking single cutaway guitar. "Paul Cleary might buy it. He had a go on it yesterday."

"It's an awful looking plank," Eva said. Naoise thought it looked fine, but nodded his head anyway.

They walked to North Frederick Street. In Walton's Eva bought a Jew's harp. Then she had a go on a drum kit, and got carried away. The manager threw them out when she played too loudly.

"Ever heard of The Big Figure? Rat Scabies? Cozy Powell?"

Naoise shook his head after each name.

"No worries. You'll soon learn."

She brought him to a place she called the basin, a little artificial lake with ducks and moorhens on it. They sat on a bench and finished the last of the liquorice allsorts. He'd noticed she liked the coconut rings most of all, and had left them all for her. She told him she lived in Stoneybatter.

"A two-up, two-down. Seven kids plus one baby equals no room," she said. "That's the arithmetic of my Johnny-free world."

She told Naoise she wished she lived in one of the houses that backed onto the basin. In the mornings she would open her window and throw out stale bread for the ducks. He told her the name of a funny looking one she was pointing at. A merganser. She gave him a record, Marquee Moon, and a music paper with dirty print that stained his fingers. She told him she had a boyfriend. "He teaches guitar. He plays a Rickenbacker." Naoise wished he knew something about electric guitars.

"You'll wish you weren't born if you tell anyone," Pelvis had said.

"T.S.O.I. The Shah of Iran," Eva said.

She was sitting between Nemo and Naoise. They were watching a gameshow, drinking the coffee Nemo had made for them. Nemo was wearing his tunic, he would be leaving soon for his shift at the hospital. Naoise guessed the letter sequences only when Eva and Nemo were stumped for an answer. Out in the garden, damp sheets flapped like dancing ghosts on the rotary line.

"I bet he's a right fucking know-all," Bandit had said.

Later, when he was alone in the room with his father, he pinched out the candle Nemo had lit on the bedside cabinet earlier, and remembered the first time they had gone to the house in Leenane. He was very young, maybe four or five, at the time. There had been a storm and a power cut. In Dublin it was never as dark as it was in the country. After his father lit the candles, he told him a story. He told Naoise that they were descended from giants, and had come from a land of giants. He called the place Jotunheim.

"Look," his father had said, pointing at the lime render wall. "You have the shadow of a giant."

After that first time, whenever they came to Leenane his father had told him stories about the giants and the old gods, their lives and their deaths.

"Stratocaster," Naoise said, close to his father's ear. "Telecaster."

He gave up after L6, and went over to the chaise longue and sat down. After a while, he stretched out under his father's dressing gown. He counted his father's breaths, and fell asleep.

In school the following day, Father McShane announced that the local schools had been invited to see an important film. Everyone cheered. After lunch break, the boys marched in double file to a girls' school on the north side of the city. Naoise walked with Fiachra, behind Maelfhiosa and Barra.

In the assembly hall, the boys and girls filed in and took their seats, and when the noise died down the film started. There were close ups of babies and foetuses, still shots of looped curettes and forceps that opened like the jaws of predatory lizards. Naoise felt dizzy and went outside to the corridor. He walked unsteadily, one hand on the paneled wall, his knees buckling. He clung to the mantelpiece of the hall fireplace and vomited into the empty grate. *Quatrefoil. Half-column. Reeded pilaster.* When he turned around, he saw Eva standing behind him, holding out a yellow handkerchief.

"So, never bunked off before?" she said, when they crossed O'Connell bridge.

Naoise told her that he would get into trouble if he didn't go back to school. She said she would write him a sick note. They walked around Trinity College to Nassau Street. She brought him to a record shop to look at records and tapes. When they went down the steps, Blue Monday was playing through the speakers. She looked in one stack, and he looked in another. He didn't know what he was looking at.

"Ready to roll?" she said, when Sunday Bloody Sunday came on.

"But this one's good," Naoise protested. "I like it."

"New Order are forever. These chumps will never catch on," she said, pulling him back up the steps.

In St. Stephen's green they laid down on the grass and watched the people go by. Naoise took off his blazer and turned it inside out and sat on it. All around them the cherry blossoms were in bloom. A string quartet was playing on the bandstand.

"It's official. I'm a bad influence. You're a mitcher," Eva said.

"Aren't you afraid you'll be caught?" Naoise said. "Someone might see us."

"Oh ee oh ee oh ee. Oh ee oh ee oh ee," she sang, "Liv-in' on the north-side dam-a-ges a person's pride."

She took off her green boots, and rolled over onto her back. She tried to play the jew's harp; and when she couldn't make a sound, she wiped it on her sleeve, and handed it to Naoise. He turned it over in his hands, hesitating, remembering the instruments he had seen in the film.

"Come on, " Eva said. "Twang the damn thing."

As soon as he brought it to his mouth, he felt queasy. It had a metallic smell. When he stood up, Eva asked, "Where are you going?" and then before he could say anything, he threw up onto the grass. While he was vomiting, Eva rubbed his back and said she didn't like the film either, but that it was better than being in class. After she cleaned his mouth, she stood in front of him and gripped his upper arms for a moment, pulling down on them sharply as if to steady him.

"Some women can't go through with it, y'know," she said. "But that doesn't make them murderers."

Afterwards, they bought toffee apples on Grafton Street. She told him that she was forming a band. She was going to be the singer and play rhythm guitar. The auditions were happening very soon, she said, in the parish hall on Prussia Street. Her boyfriend was going to be her manager. Naoise asked if he could be in the band, too. She told him it that it was going to be an all-girl band. Then she said she might make an exception for him, seeing as he was so small and peachy. This made him blush.

"What?" she said. "A reddener?"

She put her finger into her mouth, and touched his face making a hissing noise. Naoise didn't believe she had a boyfriend. At the corner of Dame street they crossed the road, and she took him to Fownes Street where she showed him a twin-necked guitar in a music shop window. As he looked at the guitar in the window, he thought it looked out of proportion, not at all as elegant as the L6 they had seen in the Rock Shop. His father had talked about proportion. How things looked in the measure of their own space.

"Do you think you'd ever play an axe like that?" Eva asked him on the way home.

"I think I'd be more of a Mosrite man," he said, pleased to imagine a world that a week before had been unthinkable.

On Friday, in his latin class, Father Jordan came in and spoke to Mr Pettigrew. Mr Pettigrew called out his name and asked him to go with Father Jordan. In the corridor, the priest told him that he had received a telephone call from his father's housekeeper, Mrs Blennerhasset, asking that he be sent home immediately.

"What about my bag? My books?" Naoise said.

Father Jordan told him not to worry about his things; he would keep them safe in the school office. The priest asked him if he had his bus fare, and Naoise said that he would walk, that his house was fifteen minutes away. Father Jordan gave him a Ritchie's mint, and shook his hand.

When he arrived home, Mrs Blennerhasset was standing on the front steps waiting for him. She told him the facts directly: his father had deteriorated; Naoise had just missed Dr Mulcahy; Nemo had come home from work to help. Before Naoise went up the stairs, she gave him a glass of milk and two goldgrain biscuits on a plate.

"Have this before you go up. No buts," she said.

He left the biscuits and drank the milk where he stood, and then he went up. Nemo was waiting for him on the landing.

"Naoise, listen to me," Nemo said, bending forward and taking Naoise by the elbow. "Today you have to be a man. You have to be strong and brave. Dr Mulcahy has put your father on a drip and on oxygen. There are tubes and tanks. He is a stubborn man. He will not go to the hospital. Your father is dying."

When Nemo said *man* it sounded like *men* to Naoise. When he said *dying h*is cheekbones glistened metallically.

When the Autumn came, Naoise's father was still alive. His eyes grew in proportion as his body shrank. Naoise's bones hurt all the time. He needed new clothes. When Summer was over he had grown five inches.

At Christmas, his father surprised them by rallying again. He stood by the bedroom window and watched Naoise and Eva throw frost-balls at each other under the trees in the garden. He played the old word games, and some new ones, too. Naoise was the second tallest boy in his year.

By Easter, his father was getting constant infections and was on oxygen all of the time. His breath was a high, wheezing rasp. Naoise's voice broke. "What is my aunt putting in your nosebag?" Eva had said. She brought him to a shop on Wellington quay where he bought size ten Doc Marten boots.

In the Summer holidays they went to Powerscourt on the bus, and hiked to the waterfall. They took a train to Wexford and went on the rides in Courtown. In a dingy studio in a lane off Bolton Street, Eva persuaded a tattoo artist that she was eighteen. Naoise held Eva's hand while the man put a blue dolphin on her shoulder. They walked along the pier at Howth, and skimmed stones on the beach at Skerries. Eva spent her savings on an SG guitar and a Vox AC30 amplifier, and she set up band auditions in the parish hall on Prussia Street. The music was frantic, loud, and disjointed. Naoise thought Eva's voice was off-key, but he encouraged her and kept his opinion to himself.

Naoise was seven inches taller than Eva, and still growing, when they went back to school in the Autumn. They measured themselves with the dressmaker's tape Eva borrowed from her aunt's needle box.

"It's six, you chancer," Eva said.

"Eight. Definitely," Naoise said.

Every evening, he sat with his father and told him about his day, where he had been, who he had been with (Eva, always). Naoise didn't like wearing the plastic gloves that Nemo gave him. He brought his pillow and blankets into the room and and took to sleeping on the chaise longue. Every morning he helped Nemo to change the sheets. Nemo moved upstairs, too, and slept in a sleeping bag on the landing floor. He was on special leave from the hospital. Outside in the garden, the chestnut trees had turned golden.

Three weeks before Christmas Naoise's father caught pneumonia for the second time and, after a small struggle, went into hospital. Naoise and Nemo rode in the ambulance with him. When he came home from St. James's in the early new year, he was so light that Nemo let Naoise lift him by himself. Late that evening, Naoise spread his books on the chaise longue, and tried to do his homework. When his father tapped his finger on the oxygen mask, Naoise came over and lifted it for him. "Big man," he said, and then he made a single, cradling motion with his arms. Naoise stretched out on the bed beside him and felt the hours past midnight empty like stones of the heat of the day.

A few days after Christmas, the snow began to fall. It wasn't the usual light and unexpected sprinkling that sometimes fell. It buffeted down until heavy drifts made the roads and streets impassable. The buses were cancelled because of the blizzard, and the city ground to a halt. Nemo insisted that Mrs Blennerhasset and Eva stay until it was safe to go home. They slept in Nemo's bedroom in the basement. Mrs Blennerhasset cooked casseroles and stews, and spoiled them in the mornings with cooked breakfasts. They played cards, and kerplunk, and monopoly. In the afternoons, Eva and Naoise built snowmen in the garden until it looked like a phalanx of white zombies was advancing on the house. When they were a week into the blizzard, they tired of making the snowmen, and one afternoon they knocked them all down with their shovels and began to heap the snow into a huge mound between the chestnut trees. Over the next few days, they cut the mound into blocks, and built a snow castle. When they were finished, the castle stood smooth and white and massive in the garden. Nemo and Mrs Blennerhasset applauded their work from behind the patio doors in the living room.

In the evenings, Nemo made pancakes and flavoured them with cinnamon. They lit the fire in the living room, and ate the pancakes while the four of them listened to records. "But some of the songs are very long, aren't they?" Mrs Blennerhasset said, after a five minute Tom Verlaine guitar solo. For her turn, Mrs Blennerhasset chose one of Naoise's father's opera records: Maria Callas and Alfredo Kraus in La Traviata. Naoise teased Eva until she admitted the arias were sort of okay. Naoise's father died a week after the last of the snow melted. Nemo and Naoise made the funeral arrangements. At the graveside, Nemo talked about his life and his creative achievements, the great friend and father he had been. He said that no man should have suffered the way he did. Naoise read a poem by Robert Frost, and Eva read from the Rubaiyat of Omar Khayyam.

The day after the funeral, Bandit and Pelvis stopped Naoise on Aungier street, near Whitefriar street church, and ordered him to hand over his money. "Well what do you know, the little queer has grown into a big queer." With one hand Naoise grabbed the front of Bandit's collarless Ben Sherman, and pinned him to the wall. With his other hand he shoved Pelvis in the face, sending him sprawling backwards on the kerb. Bandit swung a couple of heavy punches at Naoise's head, but his arms weren't long enough to make the range. Naoise drew back his fist, and just before he let fly with a straight left, Bandit closed his eyes. Naoise hesitated; but he was not afraid, he felt powerful holding the older boy up against the wall. Pelvis was standing now, but he did nothing to help Bandit. When he saw Naoise with his fist cocked and ready to punch Bandit in the face, he ran up the lane at the side of the church. Bandit opened his eyes and spat in Naoise's face. "Can't do it, can you? Fucking nancy que-" Naoise dropped him with a downward punch to the forehead, a punch he tried to pull in spite of himself.

"Oh Jesus. Don't hit me," Bandit said, covering his face with his hands. A trickle of blood ran from a cut in his hairline between his fingers. "Please don't hit me. Sweet Jesus, I'm bleeding."

On his way home, Naoise opened and closed his throbbing fist. The sky was full of low, dense clouds, and the coarse streets were ugly and grey. He had punched someone in the face. He didn't feel powerful anymore.

"Why did we leave Jotunheim?" Naoise asked his father, the last time they were in Leenane.

His father had been drawing for him a picture of a family of giants descending an icy precipice to a fertile valley of trees and streams.

"The old Gods banished us. They knew we didn't need them anymore."

"And what happened to the old Gods after they banished us?" Naoise asked, colouring the picture with crayons.

"They froze when we told them we had love."

For days Naoise and Eva had worked in the snow, building up the walls and shaping the battlements. They figured out how to cut curved blocks with the spade, and made a keep. When the keep was finished, they opened out the front wall and built a barbican. At the corners of the outer wall, they put up four round towers. They told themselves that they would stop after the towers, but then they decided to dig a shallow moat, and with a piece of garden trellis they made a portcullis. When they were satisfied that all of the elements were in place, they dipped the silver trays Mrs Blennerhasset had given them in a basin of hot water and smoothed out all of the rough surfaces. Eva borrowed Nemo's Ricoh, and took a photograph of Naoise standing in front of the keep. She told him to smile, but he didn't hear her - he was looking up to his father's bedroom window where the light was on. She took the photograph anyway, and caught in his glance a fleeting look of unbearable sadness. The camera whirred noisily - there had been only one shot left in the roll. If she had waited a moment longer she would have had to tell him to stand still, to stop flapping his arms, but she would not have had to ask him to smile. She called him over, and when he was standing in front of her, he said, "What?" and threw out his arms from his body. She put her two hands on his chest and went up on her toes; and he, misreading her intention, leaned forward and turned his head sideways to hear what she might say. He felt the little ice fragments in the fabric of her mittens when she turned his face to hers. At first, she kissed him on the forehead, a touch that lasted no more than a few seconds, and then she kissed him on the mouth. Beneath the glittering branches of the chestnut trees they held each other, each kiss more delicate, more urgent than the last. It was as if they were saying goodbye and would never see each other again. They floated above the silent cathedrals and churches, the brushed-out murmuring streets. Around them the icy blue light intensified. They closed their eyes and did not feel the cold at all.

MAI NARDONE

Rambutan!

(In English: "Ignite!") Pea jams a match under the burner. He holds on until the flame licks his nail. A cook's fingers. He feels nothing! Left hand: one spoon of oil into the wok. Two spoons ("For health," he whispers in Thai). The sheen catches the noon sun. Right hand: salt, garlic (peeled in the night, before he rubbed down Yai's feet, her heel-skin cracked and flaking like old garlic bulbs, toes purple from sleeping upright in the wheelchair), red chillies, bird's eye chillies, pork fat (a local favourite) thumbed from a jar—all into the clay mortar. Thumps it into a paste with a wooden pestle. The metal food stall rattles. The oil smokes. He scrapes a spoon, twice, around the mortar and tosses the paste into the pan. It spits. The first smell: garlic. Then the bite of chilli.

Nahm, watching beside Pea, coughs like a new-born, unaccustomed to the spicy edge of Pea's air. Pea's right foot (right toes!) finds the dial for the fan. Twists to 'HIGH POWER' (Pea practising English by labelling things). Fumes pour out into the street, away from the shop-house where Pea, Yai, and Papa live. Only Papa's been gone for a month.

Pea's left hand (slick with oil, the way Papa taught him) scoops pork bits into the hot mix. The spatula rings against the metal, scrapes and folds. Oil spills. A tongue of flame flutters about the lip of the wok. Nahm steps back but Pea doesn't flinch. Both hands (*Twelve is too young to lift the wok with one arm*, Papa always said. But soon!) jerk the wok's handle, sending pork leaping off the blackened bowl. Pea catches it. Mostly. A piece escapes, leaving a trail of gristle across the metal counter.

Pea, slowly, slowly, Pea imagines Papa saying.

But no! No time for a gentle push and fold, push and fold. The lunch hour looms. From the street: a motorbike growl. Pea reaches behind. He doesn't even look. Hands find the dark soy sauce, the light soy sauce. One shot from the left bottle, three from the right. Sugar from the bowl. Chicken stock from yesterday. He takes a handful of holy basil leaves from the stall's glass cabinet.

Nahm ladles the rice herself; she knows to find the cooker tucked beside the gas tank. As Pea breaks an egg (one hand! but he's been doing that since he was nine) into a second pan, he pauses to notice Nahm opening the rice cooker. The steam lifts into her black hair and softens the collar of her school uniform.

The egg is done. Crinkled brown corners. A cloudy yellow yolk (Yai's eyes in the morning). Nahm offers her foam container. Pea nestles the pork beside the rice, tipping the last of it with a quick heave of the wok. Too quick. The stool beneath him rocks. He tilts towards Nahm and she has to steady him with a hand to his waist. She leaves her hand there.

In the month since Papa left on a bus to some mountain temple, Pea and Yai have lost most of the regular customers. And although Nahm still buys lunch for her father at eleven every day, the shop-house is empty. The room is bare, open at the front, and now that Pea has stacked the unused plastic stools and metal tables in a corner, the entrance yawns like a mouth without teeth. They have no kitchen, only the food stall parked in the entrance, at the top of the ramp that runs onto the sidewalk. The stall is an open metal counter with two burners, four bicycle wheels (bricks wedged under the tires), and a glass cabinet that houses the fresh vegetables. Across the stall's front a sign (hand drawn) reads: Pad Krapao! Below that, in English: Stir-Fry with Holy Basil!

They serve food from eleven through seven. Pea takes orders (variations of krapao: with pork, with clams, occasionally with crispy fish) and Yai takes money, tucks it into the kangaroo pouch on her soiled orange apron. She wears a hair net too, though Pea doesn't understand why. She can't cook because she's sick. And anyway, she hardly has hair, just a few feathers of grey that sprout through holes in the netting. Sometimes Pea hates her for those tufts, and for the sour smell that he has tried to wash from her clothing. It's difficult to lift Yai without Papa, so Pea doesn't change her as often. Yai tries to help. It's not enough. She wheels around backwards, pushing on her heels because she has no strength in her arms. Yai is the mother of Pea's mother, she's part of what's left of Mama, and now she's dying.

"Pea, don't hammer the pork like that. That is not an axe." Yai has a basket of holy basil in her lap. She plucks the leaves from their stalks and drops them into the bowl by her feet. Occasionally, she puts a stalk in her mouth and makes wet slurping sounds.

"I'm not hammering. I'm chopping." Pea sinks the blade into the cutting block.

"Pea!"

"Fine," he says. "Dowager," he adds in English. He's been waiting to use that.

"What did you say?"

"Nothing," Pea says.

"You are as bad as your father, speaking English. If I could stand, I'd take the clothes hanger to you. All your hammering and oil splashing and English words will scare the regulars away," Yai says, even though there are few customers left to discourage.

But Nahm always returns. Her father, an English teacher, likes their krapao. It's understood that the fried egg (add five Baht, usually) is given in exchange for the occasional English lesson. But mostly, Pea manages with Webster's (illustrated), which Papa bought for him a couple years ago. Yesterday's new word: bommyknocker. Nahm had used it to describe Pea's wooden pestle.

Policemen have them for clubbing people into mush, she said. *Like you do with papaya.* But Pea doesn't cook with papaya. He doesn't like the crunch.

Pea likes to label things in English. They looked up 'bommyknocker', but the word was not quite right (illustration of Pea's pestle with addition of spikes). Webster's also offered 'baton,' 'blackjack,' and 'bludgeon.' He settled for a label written in pencil (impermanent), now taped around the handle of his pestle (bommyknocker). Nahm had known that Pea was looking for a name, and her father had provided one. Pea's almost finished labelling his utensil set. The unnamed: tamarind-wood chopping block, metal spatula, wok (not 'frying pan'). He thinks he'll never find an English word for the jasmine scent of cooked rice.

Papa always said that English is the language of a better place. Sometimes, during his drinking nights, Papa began to yell in English. He learnt some as a child, serving pork skewers to American soldiers on leave from Vietnam. English, Papa said, is how he became so successful, although, as Pea pointed out, no one in Udon Thani speaks English.

It doesn't matter. They know, Papa said. He uses words like 'ketchup' instead of tomato sauce, even though Yai responds with:

What is this 'chup chup'? Speak Thai!

People like the English, Papa said.

Who likes it?

My friends.

Not friends, customers.

Go crazy, Papa said in English, smiling at Pea.

Yai clapped her teeth at him. *It is your food that they like.*

It's true. Papa's was the best pad krapao on this side of Thaharn Road. In the late morning, Papa would take the stall (via motorbike addition) to the market. Pea went too, riding between Papa's arms, clutching the mirrors, hair fanned out so he arrived looking like a pop star. They set up shop on the sidewalk. *Have you ever seen anyone cook krapao this fast?* Papa would prompt the newcomers. On two burners, with two hands, Papa could cook three servings in six minutes. With Pea around: five servings. Two scoops of rice per foam container, two containers per plastic bag. Hold the containers by the edge, or risk breaking the egg yolk. If they ask, give more rice (unless it's Nahm, for whom Pea always spooned more). So Pea didn't make it to school every day, but the market is also a classroom, *Right, Pea?* Papa would say.

What did you learn about new rice today?

If the crop is too fresh, the rice is sticky. It requires less water.

And the rice today? Papa said.

Too sticky.

Papa nodded. *Good rice should be like brothers: close, but not too close.*

And with Pea at school, there would be nobody to run home for another bag of holy basil, a handful of chillies, or to force Yai (*No, I'm ready to die. I'm all set.*) to take her mud-coloured pills. Nobody (*Pea, more rice!*) to lug the steaming container against his leg, thinking: This is how Papa grew so strong.

Pea would peel, mince, mash, but Papa didn't want to teach Pea to cook. Once, as Pea reached over a frying egg, some oil spat onto his wrist and left a purple splotch. He looked at Papa's forearms, stained silver with burns.

Look, I'll grow up to be like you, Pea said, laying his arm alongside Papa's.

Papa hit him on the back of the head, hard enough for Pea to drop his rice spoon.

Don't say that. Then he picked up the spoon and handed it to Pea. *You don't want to spend your life cooking in this stall.*

But one morning, a few months ago, Pea (always too small, too short) came down to find a stool in front of the burners. Papa's eyes were still red from whisky.

We're not going to the market? Pea asked.

Not today. Let me see your fingers. Every night Pea coated his fingertips in the hot wax of the spirit house candles. Papa ran a thumb over the shiny skin. He nodded.

A cook's fingers.

Since Papa left, Pea has walked down the entrance ramp every evening to look at the motorbike. It has a single eye-shaped headlight and under its neck is a piece of engine that looks like fish gills. It was all blue once, before the paint began flaking into scales. The motorbike is too tall for Pea, but then so were the burners until Papa found Pea a stool. Now, with customers draining away like water in a basket, Pea knows he has to take the stall to the market. He needs to bring food to Papa's old buyers. He has to drive the motorbike. Pea rubs the purple scar on his leg (his only attempt to ride the motorbike alone) and remembers how the skin came away sticky where it had touched the exhaust pipe.

Nahm returns to their shop-house at dusk, unfolds a table beside the food stall, and does her homework while Pea cooks. Pea and Nahm played together as kids. Now teacher has asked Nahm to share her notes with Pea, and so Nahm comes every day to tell Pea what he's been missing at school. She keeps her notebook wrapped in a plastic bag. She writes all English words in red.

"Who are you cooking for?" she asks, taking in the empty room.

"Papa says that if you cook, people will come." Pea washes the holy basil in a bowl of water.

When Nahm works her shoulder-length hair falls around her. She brushes it behind her ear each time she turns the page. Pea waits for this. The curtain that hides her face, the hand that pulls it away, then the gradual enshrouding as the strands fall back into place.

"Did you know that the largest organ in the body is the skin?" Nahm says.

"No. What's the word of the day?" Pea says.

Nahm flips to the back of her notebook. "Stormy," she says in English. "It means the clouds during a monsoon."

But Pea likes the funny sounding ones, words that coo like a dove, like 'goon.' Or 'oyster!' (To Pea, an exclamation of pain.)

Nahm sets a bag of fruit on the counter. She takes one out. It's covered in green hairs but the skin itself is a deep red. It's ripe.

"Rambutan." She grins. "That's the English for it. My father told me."

"Rambutan?" Pea repeats.

"Yes."

Pea loves it: rambutan! Glorious. Like a war cry. Nothing like the 'ngoh' that Nahm and Pea know it as. He digs his nail under the skin and tears it apart. White flesh. Nahm bites, chewing around the seed. She hands it to him. There are teeth shapes in the fruit, in the rambutan. What a language.

A couple come up from the street to order. The seats are stacked away, so Pea tells them to wait at the bottom of the entrance ramp by the street. He fires up the burners and Nahm leans against the stall to watch.

"You've seen this a hundred times," Pea says.

"Teacher says that people learn through repetition. In school we're doing the same words over again, which means I'm learning a lot. My father says that someday I'll be an English teacher like him." She points at an ant questing along the rim of the sugar jar. Pea catches it between thumb and finger and smears it against his shirt.

"When are you coming back to school?" she asks.

Pea slows the pounding in his mortar. "I'm going to learn English by myself. I don't need a teacher." He holds up the pestle. Red paste crusts the tip. "Bommyknocker." They both laugh.

"Look." Pea lays his utensils out on the counter, right to left. Nahm touches the labels one at a time, saying the English words aloud ("Spoon. Fork, Cleaver.") until she's standing in front of the burners ("Ignite!"). She grasps the bamboo handle of the wok. She's taller than Pea and doesn't use the stool.

Pea spoons the paste into the oil. Nahm moves out of his way.

"No, stay." Pea climbs on the stool. Now they are the same height.

"Let me see those fingers." He hands her the spatula. She grips it at the top, farthest from the heat, like she's holding a skewer.

"Don't be afraid of the fire," he says, repeating what Papa has taught him.

Pea helps her, guiding the spatula with his hand (not on hers, but below it).

Push, pull, scrape and fold, Papa had told him.

"It's easier if you say it."

Nahm laughs. They repeat it: "Push, pull, scrape and fold."

"You can smell the garlic," Pea says.

Wait for the chilli. You'll know its scent in your throat, not your nose. But instead Pea had smelled the whisky caught in Papa's teeth.

"I smell it," Nahm says.

Make sure the paste is cooked through. The paste is everything.

"Now the pork. Wait!" Pea dips two fingers into the oil and presses them into Nahm's palm, kneading in an outward circle. He imagines her skin as being smooth, but actually he feels nothing. Nahm grabs a handful of pork (*Scoop, don't squeeze*) and drops it in the wok.

The hiss of frying meat draws Yai from the back room.

"Good evening, Yai," Nahm says. She lifts her hands to wai Yai.

"Teacher's daughter," Yai replies curtly. She points at the two people waiting outside. "Have they paid?"

Pea pretends he doesn't hear her.

Yai wheels closer and drums her hand against the counter. "Pea, have they paid?"

"No."

Yai always collects the money when customers take their seats inside, but this couple are waiting outside the shop-house, beyond the ramp, and Yai's arms are too weak to slow her chair on the steep decline. Pea wants to see her roll into the street. Dash herself against the pavement. He wants her to ask for help, as she never does. *My feet are sore*, Yai usually says. *This blouse, it's getting scratchy.* Then she watches Pea until he kneels to knead her bunions, young hands on old skin, both callused. Pea often notices that parts of his body are aging faster than others. Around his fingernails the flesh is bunched from years of dishwashing with hard yellow soap. Patches of hair are missing on his forearm where he has reached over an open burner. His palms are potato skins: pitted, coarse.

But Pea's skin is nothing like Yai's chest and shoulders, Pea realises, whenever he peels the blouse from her. Her bulk sinks into the wheelchair. Moles pepper her breasts. When Pea changes her linen pants, he has to work one side at a time, losing his thumbs in the folds at her waist, tugging the elastic away from the bruised flesh, down to her thigh on one side, and then the other, towing the fabric in diagonals until he has it at her ankles. Then he takes a hot towel to her. He scrapes the beads of dirt from under her arms and breasts, from her neck, from the fold of her knees. The bucket of water turns black and cold. Yai stares ahead as if it has nothing to do with her. Not her body, not his hands. She doesn't speak. Pea never touches her underwear; Yai does that herself. When they are finished she wheels herself backwards, out of his reach.

Yai glances from Pea to the customers outside.

"I can get the money from them," Nahm offers.

Yai ignores Nahm, as she always does. This is how she handles Nahm's relative prosperity.

"Pea, don't forget to take the money." Yai rolls through the shredded plastic curtain into the back room.

Pea and Nahm listen to the pork crackle. Pea lets it sit, even though the meat is overcooking. He's reminded that Nahm doesn't need to be here, that she doesn't need to earn her lunch. Pea looks under the counter. The red plastic box that holds the money is emptying faster than Pea can fill it. Soon, there will be no money to buy fresh pork, and already Pea has started on the emergency stash of frozen meat.

Nahm prepares two containers of rice.

"Did you know that they don't eat American Fried Rice in America?" She holds out the foam boxes. "Teacher said it was invented here, for the soldiers in Vietnam who missed home. That's why they put tomato sauce and hot dog in it."

"I already know that," Pea snaps. "Papa told me before Teacher told you."

"Okay." Nahm puts the containers on the counter. "I'm going home, it's late."

"Fine."

Pea takes the food down to the couple. Juice from the pork has soaked into the rice.

"It's soggy again," the man says to his girlfriend.

"My father found one for you," Nahm says when she arrives at eleven the next day. "Holysmokes," she says in English. "It means hot. Like your burner, that's holysmokes."

Pea writes it down in the back of his order log. He makes a few sketches (a flame, a wok, the exhaust on a motorbike) to remind himself of the meaning. The columns of foreign words are stained with pork grease and the bright smudge of chilli.

"You're late. I already made it." Pea hands her a container fastened with a rubber band. She's not late. Pea started the food early, worried that Nahm might notice the dwindling portions.

When Pea opened the cooler in the morning, there were only three packets of frozen meat. He thawed one, leaving it out in a bucket on the ramp like an offering, awaiting the morning sun. He watched the bundled lump unfreeze, imagining it to be a curled up animal, eyes squeezed, slowly unfurling as the sun warmed the ridges of its spine, coaxed the creature into the world that would shortly devour the it.

There are two packets of frozen meat left. Enough for a day's worth of sales at the market, if Pea can make it there. If Pea doesn't go, they'll be nothing left to cook. He'll go tomorrow.

"Too much," Pea says when Nahm hands him a bill. The red money box is empty and there's a mere fistful of coins settled like dregs at the bottom of Yai's apron pouch. "I don't have any money for change."

"Keep it," she says.

"No," Pea says, angrier than he meant it to be. "It's not my money."

"Make me two then. I'll wait," Nahm says.

"Who's going to eat it?"

"It doesn't matter."

"It matters." Pea moves away from her. He begins preparing a paste.

"Where's Yai?" Nahm asks.

"In the back, sleeping. She's sick." Yai didn't sleep well, made painful noises (*oy, oy, oy*) in the night. But Pea pretended he was asleep. He didn't want to rub balm into her back.

Nahm unties the bag of rambutan on the counter. She rips the skin off one and squeezes the whole piece into her mouth.

"It's not even English," Pea says.

"What's not?"

"Rambutan. Webster's says the word is Indonesian. It doesn't mean anything in English."

"My father says it's English." Nahm spits the seed into her palm. "Maybe Webster's is wrong."

Pea stares out at the street. He holds two things as certain: Papa's cooking and Webster's. The claim to the top title among the local krapao vendors has disappeared with Papa. Webster's, at least, Pea can rely on.

"It's never wrong." He's not watching the pestle. It strikes the mortar's edge, cracking the clay. A wedge splits from the bowl. The red pulp spills onto the counter.

Pea and Nahm stare at the mortar. Then Pea picks up the piece and slides it into place. He almost can't see the crack, but the clay falls out. He tries again. The broken piece clinks against the metal counter each time.

"It's broken, leave it alone."

"It's not." Pea jams the wedge into place and holds it there. He needs it to stay.

"Just buy a new one," Nahm says.

"The paste is everything!"

Nahm tries to take the piece, but Pea jerks away. He wipes at his eyes and walks to the back room.

"Yai, we need a new one," he cries. "I broke it and we need a new one. I need money to buy it."

But Pea knows what she'll say, he's heard it before.

What money? You drink away all the money!

This is the last time, Papa said.

You want money, you go and hawk at the market. There's no money here. Yai told Papa.

Papa opened the cabinet. The whisky was gone (hidden underneath Webster's in Pea's bedside crate).

Where is it? Papa yelled, walking at Yai. *Where did you put it?*

He took the wheelchair by the arms. He leaned over her.

You drunk! Get away. Yai clutched her bird arms to the pouch on her chest.

Papa grabbed the apron and pulled it. Yai was tugged into a bowing position, the apron's knot dragging the skin of her neck into her hair.

Let it go! she said.

Papa slammed Yai's wheelchair into the wall. Yai jerked backwards against the seat and crumpled into her lap.

(In the doorway: Pea, watching. The whisky bottle in his arms.)

Papa noticed Pea and took the whisky away. In her chair, Yai made gurgling, baby noises. Then Papa struck Pea with the bottle.

Pea's standing in the doorway clutching the triangle of mortar. He sees Yai slumped over the armrest of her chair.

"Yai!" She's limp as meat when Pea tries to lift her upright.

"Yai, get up please," he says. "Get up."

He puts his body into her. The skin pulls but Yai hardly moves. Her hair net slips off, exposing bare patches of skull.

Nahm, in a whisper behind him, "I'll call my father. He'll know what to do." Her voice jerks Pea to his feet.

"Father," he says English. Yai's hair net is in his fist. He rubs the coarse fabric against his eyes. He backs away from Yai.

"Where are you going?" Nahm says. "Pea? Stay here."

But no, no time for the ambulance. It's the lunch hour. Time to fire up the motorbike (ignite!). Pea's going to the market. That's right: cook and they will come back.

Pea bulls through the curtain. He won't cry. He feels nothing! He kicks the bricks from under the stall's wheels. It rolls at him. Pea throws his weight against it (always too small, too young—not today!). He'll show them.

It's my fault. I'm sorry, Pea. I'm so sorry, Papa will say again, like he did that last morning before he disappeared. Papa had woken to find Pea pinned under the motorbike at eleven fifteen (*Papa, we're late for the market!*), the hot exhaust against his leg, Pea's eye still shut where Papa's bottle had landed the night before.

I'm sorry.

"Pea, what are you doing?" Nahm shouts.

I need to go away. But Papa never said how long.

The stall lumbers onto the ramp. Pea, trailing, sets his heels, slows it. Not enough. A wheel squeaks. He smells hot (holysmokes!) rubber. The stall is too fast. It bowls down the ramp. Pea runs. Right hand: losing hold. He's too small. Twelve is too small. The stall drums against the sidewalk, jumps the gutter, leaps off the curb. The utensils leap with it. The mortar strikes the pavement as a hundred brown shells; the wok gets caught under a wheel and folds into a crescent; the round chopping block rolls into the street traffic. Pea catches the pestle. Bommyknocker, he thinks, waving it. In his throat: a rasping, like the bite of chilli. In the air: wet pork, sugar suspended and shimmering, the bag of fruit exploding beautifully against the glass cabinet. In his ears: a foreign language, a boy's voice, yelling, "Rambutan!"

NOEL O'REGAN

Contrails

Darragh sits outside the café and stares at the bite of sand on the near side of Dunmore Head, thinking of the wipe-outs he suffered there, the regular lungful of salt water, the stinging eyes, the blue and swollen fingers. He broke his nose for the first time in the waves below, his surfboard darting out of the water to greet him.

As Niamh breathes in the view beside him, Billy divides a brownie into squares, his Coke already drained. He eats a square and turns to Darragh.

'And what's the biggest wave you've ever surfed?'

'About ninety feet,' Darragh says, smiling.

'And how high is that?'

'Think about how high your house is.'

'Yeah.'

'And multiply it by three.'

The look on the boy's face – wide eyes, gaping mouth – is a look he's seen on the faces of most of the surfers in the Maharees this summer. When they find out who he is, what he's done. He never did what he did for that look.

Niamh rests a hand on his, making him realise that he's been tapping the table with his index finger. She slips auburn curls behind her ear. 'How far away is the house?' she asks.

Darragh smiles at her and wonders if they've reached the quasi-telekinetic point of their relationship where every gesture or unconscious act can be decoded. He's reached that stage once or twice before with other women. This time he thinks he might be ready for it.

'Not far,' he says. 'It's on the other side of the headland, before Dunquin.'

'You're sure about this?'

'What? Oh definitely, they'll be delighted to meet you.'

'You know that's not what I mean,' she says.

A coach pulls into the car park across the road and a stream of raincoats flow out. Cloudless sky, mid-twenties, but they don't trust the weather to hold; don't see it as a natural part of the landscape they're being guided through, one postcard-picture at a time. But sunny weather is guaranteed here in the last week of August. It always has been. He remembers, as a child, thinking it was a practical joke that God played – this late burst of good weather to herald the return to school.

Niamh took Billy shopping for his new uniform at the weekend. Darragh tagged along. A plump sales assistant scribbled down Billy's measurements and picked out the grey pants and jumper, the light blue shirt, the blue and yellow tie of the local Christian Brothers' school.

While Billy tried them on, Niamh leaned against Darragh. 'I still can't believe he's starting secondary school. I swear I can feel the hormones waiting around the corner. It won't be long now till he declares war on me.'

'It's all right,' Darragh said. 'You'll have me protecting you.'

She rubbed his arm and mouthed a thank you.

At the counter, Darragh handed her a fifty.

'What's this?'

'My contribution.'

'Darragh, there's no need,' she said, frowning at the note in her hand.

He kissed her on the cheek. 'Yeah, there is.'

As Darragh walks to the car park overlooking Dunmore Head, he hands Billy his loose change. 'You can get yourself some sweets with that later.' He points to the beach. 'That's the spot where I first learned to surf.'

'Down there? Can we go down? Can we?'

Signs have since been erected. DANGEROUS CURRENTS: DO NOT SWIM. For the benefit of the tourists, since everyone local knows not to swim there, that the rip-tide can snatch you away at any moment. Then it would be next parish New York. They'd already thought him mad; his swimming in those waters had only reaffirmed that view.

'We might head down later, if we've time,' Darragh says. 'We have to make a stop first.'

*

Darragh parks the borrowed Toyota Yaris in the driveway beside a four-year old Merc. He notes the extensions and renovations that crust the bungalow of his childhood: the second storey, the front patio, the conservatory where his bedroom once belonged.

He is the last one out of the car. 'See that island over there, Billy, to the right of the Great Blasket,' he says.

'Yeah.'

'What does it look like to you?'

Billy shields his eyes with his hand and squints, trying to see the island as something other than a barren squiggle of land on the horizon. Niamh smiles beside him. His words stretch out: 'A man?'

Darragh rustles Billy's brown shock of hair. 'It's called The Sleeping Man.' He points out the features of the shape floating on the horizon: the crooked nose, the beer-swelled belly, the skyward point of his bare feet. He decides not to tell the boy the island's original name – *An Fear Marbh*. The Dead Man.

Liam answers the door, the first two buttons of his pink shirt open to reveal a tuft of black chest hair. Darragh admires the smooth bridge of his own pre-broken nose on his brother's face.

'Ah, you're here,' Liam says.

'Good to see you,' Darragh says.

'The same, the same,' Liam nods. He grins at Niamh and Billy. 'Follow me in so; Margaret's put on the kettle.'

The linoleum has been pulled up since Darragh last stood in the conservatory, wooden floorboards set down in its place. New oak chairs and a table have been brought in to match. Billy eyes a plate of chocolate biscuits on the table. An Aran sweater of a tea-cosy smothers the tea pot.

Margaret enters, coffee percolator in hand. 'Sit down, sit down,' she says. 'Everyone is all right with tea? The coffee is here, anyway, if you want some.' She smiles, revealing teeth that have yellowed since Darragh last saw them. She must be on the fags again. 'And Billy, is it? Would you like a glass of orange juice? Coke?'

Billy glances at his mother, who nods. 'Coke, please.'

'Good lad. Feel free to munch away on those biscuits too.'

'Where are the girls?' Darragh asks.

Margaret responds: 'Sarah's at a friend's birthday party in Dingle, and Aoife's at camogie training. Aoife might be back before you leave.'

'I doubt she'll recognize me,' Darragh says.

'She probably won't at that, I suppose,' Margaret says.

Liam grunts. 'Pass the pot there, Margaret, would you?'

'You can reach it easy enough,' she says.

Darragh catches Niamh frown into her tea. He turns his gaze to the back garden and focuses on the shed. He nods towards it. 'Is it still in there?'

136

'Your beloved is there, alright,' Liam says. He turns to Niamh. 'No offence.'

'I have competition, do I?' Niamh asks, smiling.

Darragh grins. 'Billy, come on, there's something I have to show you.'

Inside the shed, Darragh burrows past a lawnmower, a knotted garden hose, a tasselled bicycle. He finds it leaning against the back wall. 'My very first surfboard,' he declares, dragging the white and yellow fringed shortboard into the back garden.

He worked every possible shift in Kruger's that summer to earn the money for it, the stale smell of stout and cigarettes lodged in his skin. He remembers the looks flung at him on the return bus from Tralee, the board slouched beside him. His father's baffled expression when he arrived home, the words tripping out: 'What are you, a Yank?'

Billy runs his hand over the deck, fingers the three skegs. Darragh notes how the board's in bad need of a wax.

'What's it doing in the shed?' Billy asks.

'Pride of place,' Darragh mutters, glancing in the direction of the conservatory. He slides the board against the side-wall behind the lawnmower. 'Why don't you play out here a while,' he says to Billy. 'It'll be more fun for you.'

*

As he walks into the conservatory, Darragh glances up and counts the white contrails in the sky – two, three, four. Two of the trails make a giant X over *An Fear Marbh*. No sign of Niamh, he notices. Margaret slaps her cup on the table and hisses at Liam: 'There's nothing to give, anyway'. Liam bends so low towards her he's almost bowing. Above them, the contrails flee out to sea.

Liam turns and nudges Margaret. 'Niamh seems like a nice one,' he says.

'She is; the two of them are great,' he replies.

The way Liam squints at him makes Darragh wonder if he needs glasses after all the hours spent working with his ledgers and decimal points. He is always calculating, his brother; trying to balance the books.

'Why are you here, Darragh?'

'What do you mean? I wanted to visit.'

'All of a sudden, after two years?'

'I'm still welcome, amn't I?'

137

Liam paused. 'It's money you want, I suppose.'

'Fuck sake.'

The bathroom door clicks open down the hallway. Margaret pours tea as Niamh walks into the conservatory.

'So tell us how you met this brother of mine,' Liam asks her.

'Oh, there's not much to that story.'

'We'd be interested to hear it all the same, wouldn't we Margaret?'

'I'm curious if I'm being honest,' she says.

Niamh glances at Billy soloing a football out the back. 'It's all thanks to Billy, really. At the start of the summer he plagued me about learning to surf – some friends of his had started, so naturally he wanted to give it a go. I enrolled him in the surf school out in the Maharees and Darragh ended up teaching him. We got talking, and well, one thing led to another, and that led to him asking me out for dinner.'

'Very forward of you, Darragh,' Margaret teases.

He nods. He remembers that he called over to Sheehan's, the owner of the surf school, and asked to borrow his car for the night. Sheehan laughed when Darragh then asked to borrow a shirt. His hands beat an edgy rhythm on the steering wheel as he drove into Tralee. He took her to Finnegan's, a fancy basement restaurant opposite the town park. The blue dress she wore revealed freckled arms and shoulders. She fidgeted with her placemat as she spoke about Billy, books and her own fear of the sea: 'You can never see what's beneath you; there could be anything coming and you wouldn't know.' The candlelight brought out the red in her hair. After the meal, she suggested a walk down the marina. The evening sun dressed the bay in yellow and orange. Walking on the stony shore beyond the windmill, her hand found his, and he felt the urge to be elsewhere leave him.

'And now Billy says he's going to be a surfer too, just like Darragh,' Niamh points out.

'I'm sure he'll grow out of that,' Margaret reassures her. 'Next month he'll want to be playing for Man United or Munster. That's the way with kids.'

'Maybe,' Niamh says. 'But he seems pretty earnest about the surfing at the moment.'

'He has a knack for it too,' Darragh adds. 'He's improved a lot this summer. And I didn't even know what surfing was at his age.'

'Weren't those the days,' Liam mutters.

Darragh smiles at his brother. 'And everything's good with ye?'

Liam shrugs. 'Ah sure, you know how it is. We're luckier than most, I suppose.'

'And the girls are in good form,' Margaret adds.

'That's good, that's good,' Darragh says. He glances down at his cup, rubs his thumb over the chip on the handle.

Margaret clears her throat. 'And tell us, Niamh, what is it you do with yourself?'

'I own a bookshop in Tralee,' she says, offering a smile to Margaret. 'My parents used to run it, but they got tired of it a few years ago and handed it over to me. They say they haven't read a book since.'

Margaret gives a polite laugh and Darragh thinks about the swarm of books that have gathered in his caravan through the summer. Every visit, Niamh leaves books; presents for him to pass the time not spent in the sea. What's surprised him is the comfort he's found in the clutter of hardbacks and paperbacks scattered across the carpeted floor, the table and windowsill, his bed.

'And does Billy's father help out at all?' Margaret says. 'If you don't mind me asking.'

'His father moved to Australia after Billy was born,' Niamh says, her eyes shifting briefly to Darragh. 'I assume he's still there. He never did keep in touch.'

'I see,' Margaret says.

She lifts the pot of tea and offers everyone a refill.

*

The shore waves weren't enough. As Darragh stares out of the conservatory at the sea, he thinks about the period after he moved to the States at seventeen, the buzz of competitions, the prospect of sponsorships once he started winning. How that had never felt like enough for him.

Hootie took him out on his first big wave, Mavericks. He told Darragh that it was a quiet day for it. Darragh laughed, assuming he was joking. The wave cleared forty feet easy. Darragh watched another pair power up on a Jet Ski. The surfer discarded the tow-line and dropped into the wave. He remembers thinking how it was like watching someone surf down the side of a mountain, even as the mountain caved in on itself.

'Where's Billy?' Margaret asks as she reloads the biscuit plate.

Niamh walks to the wall of the conservatory. 'I don't see him,' she says.

'He's probably around the side of the house, kicking the ball off the wall,' Liam says.

Niamh starts down the hallway. 'I'll just go check.'

Liam watches her walk to the kitchen, waits until the back door clatters against the kitchen counter. 'I suppose you haven't visited the grave?'

'Not yet,' Darragh says.

'You've had all summer.'

'I'll do it before I go.'

Liam leans forward. 'Go where? Are you taking off again? Does Niamh know?'

'No, I'm not taking off. Fucking hell, Liam. I meant before I drive back to the Maharees.'

'You're going to take Niamh and Billy to the parents' grave?'

'They can wait in the car.'

Liam claws at the stubble under his chin. He mutters something that Darragh doesn't catch; he's about to ask him to repeat it when Niamh rushes in, the exposed part of her chest blotched red.

'He's not around the side of the house or out front.'

'Don't worry,' Liam says. 'I'm sure he's only hiding. He probably thinks it's great craic altogether.'

Niamh nods. 'I know, I know. But can you help me find him.'

'Of course,' Darragh says, standing.

'There's nothing to worry about,' Margaret adds. 'At the most, he's gone up the fields, exploring. The girls spend half their lives up there and the worst thing they come across is hay fever.'

Niamh nods again. 'I know, I understand. I'm not going to turn into one of those hysterical mothers, screaming for their child. It's just strange for him to go off like this without saying anything.'

Darragh leads her into the back garden and stares up at the overgrown squares of land that Billy could be hiding in. Fields Darragh escaped into during his youth to gaze out at the open invitation of the sea.

As he walks around the side of the house, he glances into the Toyota. Nothing. He remembers the second car his brother owns, a white Opel Astra that Margaret sometimes uses. He wonders if it's in for repairs. A coach appears from the direction of Slea Head; the road towards Dunquin is clear. Darragh notes the sun dangling over the Blaskets. Liam and Margaret stand in the front doorway, watching him. He puts his arm around Niamh. In every breath she takes he can hear a faint but high-pitched wheeze.

'Everything's going to be fine,' he says.

She looks up at him. 'This is so stupid,' she says. 'This is all so stupid.'

The coach steers past and Margaret calls out: 'I double-checked the house; he's not hiding out in here, anyway.'

Darragh remembers the change he handed Billy outside the café, his freckled hand closing into a fist around the coins.

'Liam, do me a favour and drive to the café over by Dunmore Head.'

'Why?'

'I gave Billy some change earlier for sweets; he might have gone there for some.'

Niamh shakes her head. 'He'd never do something like that without telling me.'

Darragh continues: 'I'll drive into Dunquin and see if he's gone looking for a shop there.' He turns to Niamh. The rash on her chest has spread to her neck. 'You stay here with Margaret in case he shows up. More than likely, he is just up the fields somewhere, but it can't hurt to check.'

Niamh sighs. 'I'm going to kill him.'

*

Teahupoo was the first wave he surfed over sixty feet. A ridiculous swell had rushed in ahead of a tropical storm; the wave churned out surfers, shredding them on the jagged reef that waited a few feet below the surface. He remembers the sound of the lip as it pounded into the sea behind him, not being able to glance back because that moment's hesitation would cost him everything.

*

As Darragh drives into Dunquin, he keeps an eye on the roadside and bordering fields. He parks the car beside Kruger's and begins to wander among the brief scattering of houses. You have to travel the extra few miles to Ballyferriter for the privilege of a shop, but Billy couldn't have known that.

Why did he bring Niamh and Billy with him today? Was it simply to use them as a shield? Protect him from his brother's anger? A couple Darragh doesn't recognize step out of the O'Sé's house. Both wear matching green fleeces. The man nods as he passes: 'It's a beautiful day, thanks be to God.'

Darragh curses and the couple hurry on.

Maybe he wanted to show them off, his ready-made family. Prove to Liam and Margaret that he can have a regular life too. Whatever the reason, he realises that it was a mistake to have come. He has stayed clear since the funeral; it would have made no difference to remain away a while longer.

Liam never told him how long he spent on the phone that day, dialling foreign prefixes, attempting to decipher harsh accents, speaking in a slow and clear voice: 'No, I'm looking for Darragh O' Sullivan. What? No, I'm his brother. I need to speak to him. Yes, it's urgent.'

Darragh remembers the shriek of the wind outside in the pre-dawn. He stood in Hootie's garage, prepping the Jet Skis, the boards, tow-ropes and rescue equipment. He was packing the floatation vests when Hootie's wife, Jane, walked into the garage in her dressing gown. She handed Darragh the phone and dragged Hootie into the next room.

'Where the fuck are you?'

'Liam?'

'Where are you?'

'Honolulu. What's wrong?'

'Hawaii, of course you're in fucking Hawaii.'

'Liam, what's wrong?'

He coughed and his voice began to tremble. 'It's mom, Darragh. She's gone. A stroke – I tried fucking calling you – she didn't hold out long.'

Darragh stared at the garage wall. The clock hanging on it read 05:07am.

'Darragh?'

He tried to figure out what time it was back home. 'Okay.'

'Okay, what? Did you hear me?'

'I'll get the first flight back.'

He heard Liam sigh. 'Good. Okay, that's good.'

Darragh fingered the tow-rope in his hand. 'I have to go, Liam.'

'What? Oh, fair enough, I suppose. Just let me know your flight times, alright?'

'Yeah, alright. I'll talk to you later.'

After hanging up, Darragh continued to stare at the clock. It was around lunch, Irish-time. Liam would be pacing around the house, complaining; he would get great mileage out of this. Typical fucking Darragh. What the fuck is he doing on the other side of the world? Family would show up, asking if there was anything they could do, offering hands. Margaret would stack cathedrals of biscuits in the conservatory.

Hootie and Jane walked into the garage. Darragh knew from the look on their faces. Liam must have told Jane; hinted at it, anyway.

'I'm fine,' he said. He focused on Hootie. 'Have you changed the plugs yet? Has the sled been set up?'

Hootie whispered into Jane's ear and kissed her cheek. She frowned at Darragh, took the phone and retreated, probably to bed.

Outside, the wind continued to shriek. At one point, as Darragh topped up the oil, Hootie placed a hand on his shoulder and squeezed. Darragh nodded, grateful that his friend understood.

There was no way he could miss a swell like this.

*

Liam stands in the front garden, cigarette in hand, as Darragh pulls up.

'No luck?' Liam asks.

'No. You?'

Liam shakes his head, exhales.

'Where's Niamh?'

'She's gone searching up the fields. Margaret's with her, don't worry. I said I'd wait here, you know, in case he came back.'

Darragh scratches the steering wheel. 'Do you think someone might have taken him?'

'Around here?'

'It happens.'

'There's no currency in child-snatching here; it's not America. He's gone off wandering somewhere. It's what young ones do. Niamh said that he wants to be like you, after all, so he's probably getting some practice in. Disappearing is an art form the way you do it.'

'Fuck off, Liam.'

'Well, I'm just saying.'

Niamh's calls echo down from the higher fields.

Darragh steps out of the car. 'Who's living in the O'Sé's now? I didn't recognize them.'

Liam leans against the bonnet. 'They're just blow-ins from Tipperary or Longford, some god-forsaken place like that.' He sneers at Darragh.

'And sure of course you wouldn't know them; you hardly even sound like you're from here anymore. You've got that middle of the Atlantic twang now, like your voice doesn't know what direction it's swimming in.'

Darragh stuffs both hands in his pockets. 'Leave it be,' he warns.

'So where are you taking off to next?' Liam continues. 'Summer's almost up. You haven't spent a day out of summer in this country since you were seventeen, and I don't see you starting now.'

Darragh can tell that Liam is enjoying himself, needling him like this. He sits beside his brother and sighs. He knows that there's no point getting worked up; that this is what Liam wants.

He deserves the needling. It's owed to him.

He sees the envelope stuffed under the mattress in his caravan, sent by Hootie a few weeks ago, the one way ticket to Honolulu International inside. Hootie has picked up fresh sponsorship over the summer. He'll be hitting all the best waves in the coming months: Mavericks, the Cortes Bank, Teahupoo, Jaws, and he wants Darragh to be his tow-partner. He's talked about travelling to South Africa to have a go at Dungeons again. The quick sets are the killer off Hout Bay; seconds separate one ferocious wave from the next. Last time Darragh rode Dungeons he broke three ribs, four fingers and snapped his right ankle in the wipe-out. He suffered through two hold-downs – his body straining to breathe in the water, as his mind struggled to prevent it – before Hootie clawed him out.

'I'm staying here,' Darragh reiterates. 'There'll be no more big waves.'

'Like fuck there won't be,' Liam guffaws. 'I know you, Darragh. You're an addict; by the end of September you'll be off in search of your next hit. You can't deal with the real world; you've never been able to. I bet you don't even know what negative equity fucking is.'

Darragh watches the sea begin to swallow the day beside *An Fear Marbh*. He feels the sudden urge to lie on the mown grass, to crumple to the ground and sleep. He fights the urge with thoughts of Billy. Niamh is right, he thinks. This is unlike the boy. He wouldn't do something like this, wouldn't worry his mother to such an extent. Not for a few sweets or a wander in the fields.

But if there was something he was desperate to do, something he thought he wouldn't be allowed do if he asked.

Something dangerous.

The loose gravel kicks up behind Darragh; Liam's shouts follow him around the side of the house. As Niamh's cries echo from the fields above, the shed door screeches open. Darragh groans when he looks in, sees the absence behind the lawnmower.

*

The rushing ecstasy inside the barrel of an eighty, ninety foot wave – the roar, the jolt and buckle of the surfboard, the sheer force of the temple of water surrounding you, trying to engulf you, beat you down into the darkness. And time, the pull and push of it, stretching out like how he imagines it would in a car crash.

The never-ending end of it.

*

Billy will have seen the sign – DANGEROUS CURRENTS: DO NOT SWIM – and not gone in. He'll be sitting on the beach, imagining what it'd have been like to have learned to surf in such a spot: the sheen of rock on the side of Dunmore Head; the lumbering side-profile of the Great Blasket; the monks' island, Skellig Michael, an extracted tooth on the horizon.

Darragh turns right and drives through the car park on the spine of Dunmore Head. The road bends towards the beach. Across the sea, the blue café droops over the cliffs. He parks the car where the road gives way to pebbles and sand. He trudges through the sand as the sea crinkles and tears apart at its edges. He puts a hand over his eyes and squints.

He spots the surfboard fidgeting beyond the break.

Billy rests on the deck, his arms sweeping out to position himself for the next wave. Darragh walks towards him and allows the water to take his feet, his knees. He watches the sea roll in behind the boy, building as it moves towards shore. The relief he feels threatens to knock him down and submerge him.

Waiting for Billy to see him, Darragh turns his gaze to the white trails overhead. He follows their routes out to sea; he notes how they criss-cross, fade into one another and feather out among the clouds. As they clear the islands, it strikes him how beautiful they look.

In flight like that.

Star Sailor (Aistron Nautes)

"**M**y dad's heart was attacked," whispered Rana, after our teacher had settled her beside me. Her lips barely moved, impressing me. "He died. He was going to join NASA. We'd have entered zero-gravity zone and never returned."

As a nine-year-old, I'd believed her.

As an adult, I know disaster in Latin means *separation from the stars*.

The first thing I'd noticed was Rana's hair, shiny as oil. Testing its silken, choppy weight with my palms, I'd claimed her for my own. A globe-of-the-world keyring dangled from her littlest finger, blurring green and blue as it span. During play-break, we huddled against the chain-link fence. Rana confided her step-dad and mum had moved to Bolton to start a new family. Running it together made it exotic. *Newfamily.*

You'd have noticed details if you stood close. How Rana's nose curved leftward. That her right eyebrow rose a touch higher when she smiled. Mostly you'd see the inky pools of her eyes, her egg-shell thin eyelids giving the impression she had no filtering process to life. Had Rana's features been regular, would she have been better protected against the world's irregularities?

Her *newfamily* had moved into a Victorian house on the town's posh side, a contrast to our boxy high-rise. Seeing her staircase, I thought it climbed up to heaven. A secret, lovely thing was sliding along sections of the bannister, beeswax polish tickling our nostrils. I first met Rana's step-father on those stairs. A milky-skinned, compressed man with glasses and briefcase. Now he occupies the vaguest of spaces in my mind. Instead, I invite into my memories the bright pink of optimism, painted carefully over Rana's mother's full lips. Tight, hard dome of her belly. Dark hair pulled in a loose bun. As an adult wandering through the National Gallery, I would be struck by Raphael's Virgin, 'Madonna and The Pinks'. Raphael's Madonna dated from 1506, while Rana's mother was the modern-day version. Her skin colour may have been different, but the nose length, shining eyes, atmosphere of pregnant tenderness, yes, they matched.

"Girls, *pakoras* are in the kitchen."

Rana's mum's belly had been caressed, that first tea-time, like it held a prize. Rana had smiled, as if she knew what I was thinking. Her mother was kind. Welcoming. Beautiful. A blend of television and cereal packet mothers, dressed in a sari of scarlet and gold. Snacking on salty pakoras and sweet mince-pies, washed down with orange squash, a striking combination for September, I'd felt an urge to press Rana's mum's red bindi. Like ringing a doorbell. After the questions - *Only child? Your father's a porter in a block of flats? Do you like St Jude's Primary?-* Rana and I left to play hide-and-seek among cardboard boxes.

"Is this for when you've got people to stay?" I'd asked, walking into a space under the eaves. A tatty brown guitar case rested on an unmade bed. The bottom corner of a Bolton Wanderers' poster peeled off the wall.

"It's Cooper's."

"Who's he?"

"Step-brother." Tucking one leg behind the other, Rana chewed shiny hair. "My brand-new step-brother."

"Oh. Didn't know you had one."

"He's not proper," explained Rana, winding spittle-wet hair around her finger, "he doesn't live with us. But Martin, um-" Rana took a breath, "-*pitaaji* Martin, says Cooper will be visiting, so he's allowed to keep stuff here."

"Oh," I repeated, stupidly. "What's he like?"

"I saw him at my mum and sted-dad's wedding," she said. "He lives with his mum on a boat where he sleeps and eats. He's older."

A fat fly knocked into the guitar case, making a popping sound. I wondered about a brand-new older brother, arriving ready-made. It made me think of Ikea flatpacks. My mum complained my dad never followed instructions because they turned out wonky.

"I have photos of my dad before he died," said Rana suddenly. "My *baapoo* dad. Before I'd fall asleep, he'd tell me a story."

This was said uncertainly enough to get me interested. "Go on."

A pause, then Rana spoke in a voice deeper than normal.

"Little Rana. It is a dark night." A spurt of giggles, then Rana was serious. "Stars are lighting the sky up like day. A brand-new rocket is going into space. Unseen by anyone, a little girl has climbed into the outer engine. She is hiding, quiet as a mouse, in the shuttle box. In the morning, the space rocket will enter zero gravity and she'll be the first little girl to count the constellations and discover new galaxies. Some of them will be named after her."

In the silence, the fat fly hit the sky-light, *pop-pop-pop,* trying to escape. Rana said, "That little girl, she goes to the moon and explores all these new planets never seen by human eyes. It's brill. Mostly, she floats in zero gravity."

I said nothing. Even then, I knew there was nothing I could add.

I should mention lightness. Lightness of being is what's conjured when I think of young Rana. Skipping, hopping, jumping, twirling – these were Rana's favourite actions. One morning she came into school, shiny hair alive with static, wide grin splitting her face.

"Martin – I mean, *babaji's* – sticking them on my ceiling!" She clutched a crinkly bag of glow-in-the-dark stars and planets like they were treasure, eyes lit like inky dark bulbs. I only smiled with superiority because my cousins had them.

* * * *

Everywhere in the streets, ghosts give out memory jolts of Rana. Vapours from the past. Down the parade, gaggles of teenage girls laugh and jostle, meaty thighs exposed, interlinked elbows forming 90 degree angles. One teenager is pale, more aloof than the others. Catching me watching, she hawks and disappears inside a shop of mostly-nude mannequins. Still. She'd had something of Rana about her, been that same vigilant, peaky age as Rana when she'd leaned against her bedroom wall, announcing,

"Now that astronauts have stopped going to the moon, it's as if the world has stopped dreaming. As though," she'd thought for a moment, considering, "we've stopped searching for our *future and our past*."

"What you saying? Nah Rana, you're talking daft again." We were on the floor, eating oven pizza and chips from takeout boxes, days of home-made *pakora* over. I was angling a shoelace of mozzarella into my mouth. Unable to connect with the force of Rana's longing, I licked grease from my lips and began flipping through T.V. channels. By then, Rana's mother's bright lipstick had disappeared. She'd also had her fourth miscarriage. As if taking up those missing babies' places, Cooper had moved in, spreading himself and his belongings. The large Victorian house, once welcoming, was cloaked in uncertainty, less in kilter with its foundations. I wasn't as envious as I'd been. I'd asked Rana once about her family, her Indian side. Blankly, she'd said it wasn't her real dad's fault he'd been white. Like it wasn't her mum's fault she was Indian. Both of these things were *facts*. Like air, or water. Or stars. But Rana's Indian family had told Rana's mum she was dead to them for marrying 'outside'. Quietly, Rana said it was like they'd won because her dad was dead and her mum couldn't marry someone Indian, even if she'd wanted to, because in her mum's family's eyes she wasn't alive. Really, if you thought about it, Rana added, no-one had won. Then she switched on the Science Discovery Channel. I returned to French-plaiting my hair.

By the time we were 13, Rana and I were meeting in neutral territory, in the skate area or the park café, pleading cigarettes off strangers. In the colder months, we ended up at mine, where she'd eat dinner and sleep over.

We also experimented. Ouzo, brandy, gin and vodka – the last because it was undetectable on the breath, although we often smelt it on Rana's mum. Drinking was joyous, allowing a freedom of being, of expression. I told Rana once that I thought drinking was like being in zero gravity, a place relaxed enough to think large, loose thoughts. She'd held my hand, until I felt uncomfortable and pulled away.

It was during the yawning gap of Year 9 summer holidays that I noticed blackberry-dark patches drifting across Rana's skin. They came and went, like cloud formations. But when a collection of dark clots ringed Rana's throat, I came to, as if slapped. Almost arrogantly, Rana said they were skate-boarding scars. Battlescars.

But that night, a near-empty, decent-sized bottle of vodka between us in a moonlit playground, our faces plugged to the raw brightness of stars above, Rana said they were Cooper's. Rucking up her t-shirt, hair curtaining her face, Rana showed me her chest and back. Her outline looked frail, something that could easily disappear. I felt jolted, faced with a story surely belonging to someone else, not Rana. Then I understood. Stories were what we had. They were a currency of sorts. Hesitatingly, I began the familiar line,

"It's a dark, dark night, but the stars are out in the sky, lighting up the galaxy, making it bright as day..."

After a moment, Rana joined in, voice carrying in the clear cold air,

"...a beautiful, bright, summers day, although it's the middle of the night..."

"...a brand-new rocket is going into space in the morning. A little girl has climbed into the engine..."

"...hiding quiet as a mouse in the shuttle box..."

"...when the space rocket goes into zero gravity..."

"...she'll be the first little girl to go into space."

Kneeling, I put my arms around Rana, matching my forehead to hers. For a while, we rocked gently, her on the swing, me with my knees digging into tarmac. Lit by the flare of the street lamps, Rana's treacle-shiny hair was a soft halo. I began pacing, threatening to smash Cooper's head in with the vodka bottle. After a while, I was sick along the slide. Later, tucked up in bed, I heard the dawn chorus of birds, impossibly loud, impossibly sweet.

The next morning, Rana reverted.

"Mandy, it was the vodka. I got carried away. I'm sure you won't worry my mum. She and Martin are going to Spain for a last IVF attempt. That's what she's thinking about, yeah?"

"I still don't understand why you're covering up for that shit-head," I said. "It's sick."

But Rana was stubborn.

With everything sun-glazed and beautiful, I caved. Wasn't being drunk sort of like that? Getting into a state where you told stories and got lost in fantasy? I too, got bruises from skate-boarding. Didn't I? Although not around the neck. But that was the more likely, and likeable version. Next time I heard Rana boasting at the skate-park about doing bigger airs, longer grinds, better ollies, I turned away from her narrowing eyes.

And I avoided asking about her family. As if I knew the slightest mention would bring the whole house of cards down. You see, I realise there was a partnership to what we did. An *enabling*. But you didn't have to be a mind-reader to see Rana's mum was sinking fast. At parent's evenings she turned up wearing stained, baggy skirts and jumpers and she'd grown bigger, not pregnant bigger, but fat. Gone was the wide smile, softly-shining hair. *Acutely depressed* would be the medical term.

But Rana got on so well with things that four years later we were sitting in the park, me wondering whether I could invite Cooper to my 17th birthday party. The drrings of bikes and scuddings of clouds made everything feel safe. I'd bumped into him the week before at Budgen's, where I was cashier and shelf-stacker. Cooper had finished university, and he wore his stubble with the lived-in sexiness (I thought) of a leather jacket. There was a bitten, plumpness to his lips that made me assure him Budgen's was temporary.

"I've got three weeks to go," I'd said. "It's not bad. I'd go mad if I had to stay on."

Cooper had winked. "With your brains that won't happen. Bet you're studying something hard-core, really *out there*."

I'd loved him assuming I was going to university. Mum and dad hadn't. I'd surprised them with a final push before mocks. But I'd done well, and mum's aunt had left some money.

"Actually yeah, I'm doing Art History."

"Cool. And you're working over the summer. Shows you've got independence."

Cooper had a way of putting a positive spin on things. The only less than perfect moment was asking about his dad and mum.

"Usual," Cooper said, with an edge. "Dad's a workaholic, mum's a partyholic." He'd looked at me slyly. "Then there's Rana's mum."

As if the letters were in bright colours dancing between us, I knew exactly what kind of '*holic* Rana's mum was. An image of her in a sloppy jumper appeared, grainy and burnt as an old photograph. It made me feel dirty. But a moment later Cooper cuffed me goodbye and I returned to stacking, replaying that grazing touch on my shoulder.

"So, Rana," I now cleared my throat nervously. Aware of the wrongness of what I was about to ask. "I bumped into Cooper. His mates are inter-railing. He's on his own. But if you don't want family, it doesn't matter. Obviously."

Rana put on oversized sunglasses and lit a cigarette, and I felt the vertigo of falling through a trapdoor italicized with 'traitor'.

She said, "I used to have a phobia. Ventriloquism."

"Ventriloquism?" I was relieved. "That's weird. When does anyone see a ventriloquist?"

"A random kid's show with my dad. My real dad. In our old village church hall. I ended up crying when the doll bit my ear."

"Freaky," I said. "You were young, though? I mean, if your dad was still alive?"

"Died soon after. It was one of the few outings, just me and him. Another reason I don't like ventriliquism."

I tried to imagine Rana with her dad, the one whose photograph she kept in an A4 envelope under her mattress. Instead I saw the stiff upright grey of her step-dad, spectacles blankly flashing like a machine-man.

"Cooper knew. He'd got himself a ventriloquist's doll, given it a name. Ginger George." Lighting a cigarette, Rana passed it. I took a deep pull, filling my lungs. "A clever touch was Cooper refitting one of the eyes so it hung upside down. One Saturday afternoon, while ma was upstairs resting, I found Ginger George on top of the settee. Not doing anything. Just sitting. Still, I had to cross my legs because I needed to wee. But ma had been telling me I needed to look after myself, so *without actually questioning its presence,* I approached Ginger George. I was an inch away when the room filled with some fucking weird song screeching 'Marjory Razor-blade'. Cooper had been behind the sofa, waiting to press play."

My body went cold. "*Bastard.*"

"So I pissed and shat myself. Literally."

"Bloody hell."

"I never told anyone. Cooper said I was a dirty little Paki. Ginger George was proof."

"Proof of what?"

"I needed to take my depressive mum back to my own country. I didn't know the meaning of depressive. I understood Paki."

"Jesus Christ Rana, it's not like you're properly Indian. I mean," I said, trailing, "you don't celebrate the festivals we learnt at school."

I feel pain, physical pain, when I recall those words.

Rana continued, "I wouldn't have told. I stuffed my dirty clothes into a plastic bag and crept to the outside rubbish bin. Then I washed the floor. Not well, because I had to blame the cat."

Dazed, I listened to the drrring of bikes. They sounded more like warnings.

Rana tenderly unwrapped a block of skunk, her hand slightly shaking. "Sunlight takes 8 minutes to reach us. Did you know?"

"I didn't." I licked my lips.

"That's just in our solar system. No, what astronomers are seeing aren't galaxies now, but lights from galaxies past. They're looking for the Big Bang. Evidence. The Beginning of Everything."

I laughed uneasily. "God, where are you getting all this stuff?" I was worried for Rana, disturbed that she wasn't anchoring herself to the earth like the rest of us.

She ignored me. "Our bones have calcium," she said conversationally. "Stars are also made of calcium. Do you want to know my theory? That we were once all part of each other. Our cells, chemical matter... do you get what I'm saying, Mandy? *We came from the stars.*"

"Fuck," I said. I paused. "Rana, are you talking science... or poetry?"

"Both," she said. And she stuck a spliff between her lips and tilted her head to the sky.

Cooper was never mentioned after that.

Twelve months on, Rana had secured a place at Durham University to read Physics. I was going to Sussex. Before leaving I tried, awkwardly, to talk. Of course, it was too late. Rana had put up a wall, impressive in its finality. Without much effort, I gave up.

I also had my own battles. Dad and I were locked in constant aggression, perhaps not a surprise in itself. My mother was lassoed into playing reluctant referee. Home was a ragged, fraught place to be. In my defence (if I have one, which I'm aware I don't) Rana seemed no different from anyone else. A bit eccentric, occasionally moody. And with an immediacy which made it appear inevitable, we lost touch on becoming undergraduates. The separation was tinged with relief.

So perhaps you can understand the shock, nine years later, of opening my door in Upper Holloway to find Rana standing by my gate wearing a mouldy-looking woolly jumper and dirty, construction-worker type jeans. Most painful of all was her shaved head. That weighted mass of shiny, heavy hair, razed to the scalp. I admit I had to physically force myself back through the years to connect with this strange figure. Dark brush-strokes ringed her eyes. Rana stepped forward. With a light, nervous touch, she kissed me. I caught her familiar, faint tea-rose smell.

"Mandy," she said, diffidently. "Am I disturbing you?"

"Not at all," I said. "Come in. What a surprise." And I wheeled my bicycle backward into the hallway. How she'd found me, I wasn't sure. I'd moved cities, addresses, swapped partners. I was barely the same person. Had we met in a shop or on the high street, it would have been different. But there was something self-conscious about Rana appearing on my doorstep, without any preamble of having "been in the area". I flicked on the kettle and her charged presence filled my small kitchen. She didn't touch anything, but the intensity of her packed-in protons and neutrons set me on edge.

She clocked the photographs on the fridge (a couple of old girl-friends, no-one current, no children) and assorted art prints hanging on the wall. Then, as if presenting the dark to my light, Rana told me her mum had died of a brain aneurysm, almost twelve full months after Martin, her step-dad, had cited irreconcilable differences and swiped most of their shared assets. Not that Rana's mum had owned much to begin with. Throughout all this, Cooper's absence from the conversation sat easily between us, the presence of a voided entity.

Ironically, it was something in my own life which nudged us to the subject of space. Having studied Art History, I was now a freelance arts editor and writer. I was reviewing a book cataloguing an artist's studies of outer-space in oil, acrylic and soft pastel mediums. Moving the book aside, I asked Rana if she was still interested in space. Expressions gathered speed and shifted across Rana's face with the suddenness of mercury. She turned towards the window, to the garden. Flatly, as though the opening line to a song or a prayer she knew and hated, she spoke. "Four."

"Sorry?"

"Four is the number of bedroom doors refitted."

I put down my mug as she gathered speed.

"Two is the number of chipped teeth, one is the black eye, endless was the dread of my mother miscarrying again if I told. Skate-boarding was my excuse. Covered just about everything. Although really, she must have known."

My knees clamped together, my hand lay over hers, as we listened to the faint chirp of birds while our tea cooled beside us. An image of a little girl appeared, bandaging herself until her face was wholly, whitely covered. Then she disappeared.

Looking back, I suppose Rana's pregnancy was obvious. I thought she'd knitted her shapeless jumper herself, its ugly earthen rawness coinciding with her shorn scalp. She'd lacked that palpably pregnant air most women have. But then, she'd always carried her body as an after-thought, the real axis of her, the weight of her, in her mind.

After she left, I registered that no phone numbers or email addresses had been exchanged. My brain was at the stage where things weren't processing. A recent girlfriend had broken up with me cruelly, someone on whom I'd been pinning long-term hopes. I'd been stupidly hoping we would live together, set up a life. And of course, I was not to know I wouldn't be seeing Rana again.

It was with surprise that in the days and even weeks afterward, I found myself trying to recall the story Rana's dad used to tell her at night-time. Her real, *Baapoo dad*. After the little girl had climbed into the space shuttle, did she fly and explore space, or was she discovered and made to stay on earth, bound always to look up through the small, tight circle of a telescope? It bothered me that I didn't know.

Three months later, one spring morning, a wicker basket was left by my back door, the kind used to deliver posh fruit. Pinned to its handle was a crisp white envelope. Unlike everyone else, I wasn't surprised by my response. It felt natural, expected. Written in the stars.

Mandy,
Meet Valentina.
She has been named after Valentina Tereshkova, the first woman to reach space. Space, as you know, is infinite. It is my prayer and my hope. Now I will feel it in my soul. I've asked myself, since there was failure in my protection, what makes me think I could protect Valentina? Mandy, your trust in humanity remains. I entrust you with Valentina.
Yours, in memory.
Rana.

Motherhood is a startling experience. Sleep deprivation, adoption papers, responsibility settling like a heavy cloak around my shoulders wherever I turn. Looking at baby Val, my child born of the stars, my *newfamily*, I wonder about the colossal jolt Rana will have experienced as she hit that place called zero gravity. Watching Val's tiny hands opening and shutting, face responding to sudden, uncertain connections between synapses, I think of Rana in that weightlessness. An Icharas, an astronaut, a modern day star-sailor, floating in a galaxy where the stars have made everything safe as a summer's day.

NICHOLAS RUDDOCK

Polio

In 1953 the polio virus hovered over the summertime streets of Toronto, it multiplied in the warmth of slow-moving creeks and in the shallow sands of Ward's Island, in rainfall it slipped down from the canopy of maple, elm, heat and cicadas, vaporizing into random bedrooms thought secure, tasteless on the tongues of those who lay commingled there. Over breakfast we heard radio accounts of children slumped like rags, breathless, cyanotic, living out their lives within relentless metal carapaces, "iron lungs" pushing, pulling at the paralyzed chest itself incapable of moving air, and those children who had been rendered voiceless by tracheotomy used their teeth to go *click-click-click* drawing the attention of nurses to their plight (real or imagined) and the *click-click-clicking* ratcheted up as the sky darkened with ozone and thunder and the threat of power failure which would bring parents, neighbours and passers-by unimpeded to the open wards in a rush of fear-of-smothering, the starch white dresses of the nurses "like moths" amidst the to-and-fro swishing of tubes, the children lying as though beheaded, the sick quarantined, the healthy (you and I) taken to the cedar-filled air of Inverhuron where the second of the Great Lakes beat against a series of reefs straight out from shore, where in the last shelf of rock (before the lake dropped off to what seemed to us to be fathoms of darkness) we could see the petrified coral bodies of tiny crustaceans, locked into their airless world centuries before polio.

MICHELLE WRIGHT

Fine

Twenty-five degrees. Twenty-six degrees. Twenty-seven degrees.

Southerly wind. South-westerly wind. Northerly wind.
Fine. Sunny. Overcast. Isolated showers. Late change.
Melbourne. Adelaide. Cairns. Darwin.

It's clear he has a background in radio. His voice is balanced, his diction exact. He needs something to occupy his time now he's retired.
And the money comes in handy.

Even after the diagnosis, he insists on going in to the recording studio for at least an hour a day. Towards the end, they set the equipment up in the dining room of his house.
He's just finished recording the last words on the list when the tumour says, "It's time" and he falls from his chair.

Twelve years later, it's still his voice that announces the daily telephone weather: towns, temperatures and wind speeds, edited together seamlessly and updated each day.

From time to time, in the lonely hours of the night, his widow dials the number of Teleweather.

Fifty-five cents a minute to hear the familiar voice travelling the country: town by town, hot spells to cold snaps, drought to deluge, season by season.

Perth. Twenty-nine degrees. Mostly sunny. Late thunderstorm.
Alice Springs. Thirty-three degrees. Sunny. South-easterly winds, gusty at times.

Sydney. Twenty-five degrees. Morning fog. Westerly winds at thirty kilometres an hour.

When her children ask, "Are you happy?" she smiles and smoothes the tablecloth.
"I'm fine," she replies. "Keeping busy."

But, at the end of the month, when she opens the phone bill, she sees just how much she's been missing him.

SARAH BAXTER

Locked In

I hear the suck of plimsols, then a *tink* of plastic button against the bed frame as you lean over for evening checks. I inhale your tea break cigarette and think my greeting – *Hello Sheila.* I hear the rip of tape – first my left eye, then my right. Two fingers on my radial artery measuring what remains. You slip one hand under my shoulders, the other beneath the sheets, and roll me like a dead man. The memory of my balls tightening roars forward and dissipates as you push the pill up my arse.

Where do you go at six o'clock? Who lies next to you when the night shift comes on? I see bruises. Do your colleagues think you're clumsy? And what happens every second Thursday evening to make you sing all Friday long? Who inspires this tinny chorus?

I wouldn't have looked at you twice when I lived under the sky. My preferences tended to student types with loose limbs, and brunettes with easy mouths – too many to name. They run as a film reel when I need them, before they merge into one composite, celluloid face.

The red capillaries behind my eyelids flick dark as you snap off the fluorescent light. *Night, Sheila.* You strike up the earworm of your Friday love song and pad away. I feel the heat of the pill kicking in. I think *You're nothing to me* and settle back, deep under my skin.

JOSEPHINE ROWE

Ern Kiley's House

We grew up watching them boys free-diving the drowned town. That was weekends. We weren't so gutsy. They wanted to get down deep enough to look in the windows of the houses that got left behind. Like there were people still down there living watery ghost lives or something. Sitting down to breakfast at the table like normal, but when you pour out the cereal it just goes everywhere like fish food. That's what they wanted to see, things like that.

They rowed out with big stones in the bottom of a tinny, and tipped over the side with these stones hugged tight to their skinny chests, so they'd sink down fast and easy. There'd been government money to move the whole town out of the valley before they flooded it for the Hydroelectric. But some of the houses were too rickety to hoist onto the trucks. Ern Kiley's house was strong enough but he said, *Bugger it, leave it,* so they did. His wife and son had died there the summer before and he was done with living in it.

It was the Kiley house them boys were diving down to all them years ago. When the drought came it rose out of the lake mud like a sludgy, shipwormed beast. We put on old shoes and walked out over the cracked mud, across the not-lake. Right up to the empty windows to see if the table was still set. All we saw was a roomful of rocks.

PAUL STEPHENSON

Lincolnshire

Keith was at mine when Doris arrived, and had I heard? Doris said she'd have to tell people sooner or later and Keith said, 'better sooner than later'. I nodded, darted to the kitchen and unscrewed a Bulgarian red. Doris said, 'ooh that's a nice drop', arguing with Keith if it was 5D or 5G and what they'd pressed in the lift, Doris insisting, 'no it wasn't Keith', but eventually they agreed it was brand new next to maternity.

Doris announced they'd made a mask of her so the special waves could get working Tuesday week while Keith said the nurses were Thai and couldn't be friendlier. Doris added the doctor was the spitting image of that nice-looking fair-headed chappy from off the Titanic and that Keith'd take her up there each morning but couldn't run her to Lincolnshire. Keith said he wasn't comfortable going that far.

Doris rubbed her throat, said it was getting on for a fortnight since she'd given up the smokes and Keith winked, said it hadn't stopped her fuming at him and whenever she went away he got promoted to boss but once back soon got demoted, received his orders from above. Doris coughed, said, 'it'll be sore for a while' and Keith insisted she 'keep ever so, ever so still'. I poured Doris a last drop and sipping she said, 'I'll sleep tonight', sank back in the sofa and it all went quiet, as if the waves were busy doing their job.

DAVID STEWARD

The Edge of the Woods

You'll have to decide whether this story has a happy ending. When I was seven, my parents took me on holiday to Devon, before satnav and mobiles. Late one evening, we were looking for accommodation, and came across a small hotel in woodland.

"It's closed," Dad said. "There's a door unlocked round the back."

He found a fuse box, but the electricity must have been cut off. There was water in the taps and cisterns. He wanted to move on – we couldn't use the place without permission – but Mum was bullish.

We ate a picnic supper and I dozed under the sheets while they played cards by the camping lantern. During the night, I woke to movement and saw Dad at the window, agitation in the small actions of his hands on the sill. He held up his watch to catch the grey light.

In the morning, Mum wouldn't be hurried. She stopped in the bar to take the pump clip off a handle. On the badge was a stag, antlers raised against rays of white light. All the way to Porlock, Dad was tight-lipped.

And that's it. There was no great drama, but it comes back to me as strongly as moments of high emotion or little humiliations of childhood. It was as if, walking in the shelter of the woods, I noticed that the alignment of trees gave a vista, down which I had a glimpse of what lay beyond: the happiness and anxiety, the loss.

Biographies

Wendy Cope read history at Oxford University and taught in London primary schools for fifteen years. She has been a freelance writer since 1986, when her first book of poems, *Making Cocoa for Kingsley Amis*, was published. Her fourth collection of poems, *Family Values*, appeared in April 2011. She has also written for children and edited several anthologies. Her work has won awards on both sides of the Atlantic. In 2010 she was appointed OBE in the Queen's birthday honours list and she is a Fellow of the Royal Society of Literature. She lives in Ely.

Michèle Roberts is the author of twelve highly acclaimed novels, including *The Looking Glass* and *Daughters of the House*, which won the WH Smith Literary Award and was shortlisted for the Booker Prize. She has also published poetry and three collections of short stories, most recently collected in *Mud* – stories of sex and love (2010). She is Emeritus Professor of Creative Writing at the University of East Anglia, a Fellow of The Royal Society of Literature and a Chevalier de l'Ordre des Arts et des Lettres. Michèle Roberts lives in London and in the Mayenne, France.

David Swann has had five successes at the Bridport Prize, including three stories featured in his debut collection, *The Last Days of Johnny North* (Elastic Press, 2006). His book, *The Privilege of Rain* (Waterloo Press, 2010), was shortlisted for the 2011 Ted Hughes Award, and features reflections upon his work as a writer-in-residence in a prison. A former newspaper reporter, he now lectures in English & Creative Writing at the University of Chichester. In 2013, David Swann gained his second success in the National Poetry Competition. He divides his time between Brighton and Hove, where he is hard at work on a trilogy of novels and a book of micro-fiction.

Dima Alzayat was born in Damascus, Syria and raised in San Jose, California. Currently she lives in Edinburgh, Scotland where she is pursuing an MSc in Creative Writing at the University of Edinburgh. Her articles have appeared in the *Los Angeles Times*, *Variety Arabia*, and *The Skinny*.

Virginia Astley is a songwriter and musician who from a young age has appreciated the process of writing, often working things out by writing them out. Her collection *Solvitur Ambulato* was published in *The New Writer* earlier this year. She has won prizes in several competitions including: *The Frogmore, Ver Poets*, East Coker and Manchester Cathedral. She has an MA in Creative Writing from Bath Spa University and is currently completing her book: *Keeping the River*. This is a narrative non-fiction based on the River Thames and the lives of those who work and live on the river.

Sarah Baxter is clinically addicted to knitting. She has more jumpers than novels but that will change because her success with the Bridport has spurned her on to take six months off work to write.

Daisy Behagg grew up on the south coast of England. She completed a BA and MA in Creative Writing at Bath Spa University, and has previously had work published in *The Rialto, Poetry Wales, The North, Ambit, The Warwick Review, Poetry Salzburg Review* and *New Linear Perspectives*. In 2012 her poems were runner-up in the Edwin Morgan Prize and highly commended in the Bridport Prize. She now lives in Bristol while completing her first collection of poetry.

Richard Berengarten (formerly known as Burns) was born in London in 1943, into a family of musicians. He has lived in Italy, Greece, the USA and former Yugoslavia. The five volumes of his *Selected Writings* are published by Shearsman, including *The Blue Butterfly* and *The Manager*, with two more forthcoming: *Manual* (2014) and *Notness* (2015). In the 1970s, he founded and ran the international Cambridge Poetry Festival. He is recipient of the Eric Gregory Award (1972), the Keats Memorial Prize (1974), the Duncan Lawrie Prize (1982), the Yeats Club Prize (1989), the Jewish Quarterly-Wingate Award for Poetry (1992), the international Morava Charter Prize, Serbia (2005), and the Manada prize, Macedonia (2011). His work has been translated into more than ninety languages.

A former Arts Council of Great Britain Writer-in-Residence at the Victoria Adult Education Centre, Gravesend (1979-1981), Visiting Professor at the University of Notre Dame (1982), British Council Lector, Belgrade (1987-1990), Royal Literary Fund Fellow at Newnham College, Cambridge (2003-2005) and Project Fellow (2005-2006), he is currently a Praeceptor at Corpus Christi College and Bye-Fellow at Downing College. He also teaches at Pembroke College, Peterhouse, and Wolfson

College, Cambridge. He has three children and two grandchildren. He lives with his wife Melanie Rein, a Jungian analyst.

Lisa Brockwell spent a large chunk of her adult life in England. She now lives near Mullumbimby on the north coast of New South Wales, Australia, with her husband and son. This year, her poems have been published in *The Spectator* and *Australian Love Poems 2013*. She is working towards a first collection.

Publications: 'Waiting for the Train' *The Spectator*, 27 July 2013, 'The Ballad of Monday Morning' *Australian Love Poems 2013*, Inkerman & Blunt, 2013 and 'The Bounty', *Snakeskin*, 2011.

Julian Broughton was born in 1957. He studied English and Music at Cambridge, and has worked for most of his life as a musician, composing, teaching and performing. An accomplished pianist, he particularly enjoys chamber music and working with singers. Until recently he was employed by the University of Sussex to convene their part-time BA in Creativity and the Arts. Compositions include a symphony, commissioned by Horsham Symphony Orchestra and premiered in 2010. A particular interest in setting contemporary poetry has led to collaborations with Peter Abbs, Abi Curtis, Kim Lasky, and Paul Matthews. Julian Broughton has written poems since childhood. 'A Good Fit' was published in *The New Writer* (no.99), and 'After' was published in *Resurgence* (no.279).

Sheila Crawford, born and brought up in a Sussex village, has taught languages in Zambia, Oxfordshire and Northumberland. Her early published writing includes two children's novels *(Joe* and *The Foundling* – OUP), articles for the *Education Guardian* and reviews for *The Listener*. Recently she has received awards from NAWG – three first prizes in the poetry category and several runners-up certificates for adult short stories. She was short-listed in a previous Bridport flash fiction competition.

Jenny Danes is originally from Braintree in Essex and currently lives as a student in Newcastle. She found her passion for writing through an active creative writing group at her sixth-form college, and is now in her first year at university studying English Literature and German.

Benjamin Dipple lives in Sussex. He is married with two children and works as a builder. He is also trying to write a book. He is unpublished.

Sallie Durham lives in West Sussex with her family and assorted pets, and works as an English teacher. She is a night writer of poetry and fiction. Her short poem 'Other People's Lives' won the Plough Prize 2011 and her story 'The Elephant' won The Lightship International Flash Fiction Prize 2012. Sallie's work has been published in *Lightship Anthology 2*, *Heart Shoots* poetry anthology from Indigo Dreams, *The New Writer* and *What The Dickens?* magazine and anthology.

Emily Goldman is a writer, composer, pianist, and teacher in New York City. She is currently pursuing an MFA at NYU's Graduate Musical Theatre Writing Program.

Doreen Gurrey is married with five children and teaches Creative Writing at York University's Lifelong Learning department. Formerly, she taught English and Drama in secondary schools followed by work as a tutor in Adult Literacy for York City Council, teaching adults with no formal qualifications.

Kerry Hood is from Bournemouth and though she's lived in Bristol since gaining a first in English Literature, the Dorset coast permeates her work. A recent story, 'Of All The Whole Wild World', was recorded live and broadcast on BBC Radio 4. Awards include 'Two Ticks' (also BBC Radio 4), 'Space Cadet', 'Every Other Sunday And Where I Go', 'Yaroops', 'Magic Thing', 'The Man Who Turned A Stone Bridge Into A Hammock' and 'Olympic Café'. 'People Like Her' appears in *The Bristol Prize Anthology Vol 5* (Bristol Review of Books Ltd). Other stories have been placed/shortlisted in The Bridport Prize, BBC Opening Lines, The New Writer, Frome Festival of Literature, Mslexia, Lightship Publishing and Flash500.

She's written ten plays, including *Meeting Myself Coming Back* for Soho Theatre (Oberon Books), *Caution! Trousers* (Stephen Joseph Theatre), *Talking for England*, (Ustinov Theatre Bath) and *My Balloon Beats Your Astronaut* (Tristan Bates Theatre).

'Imagine one of Beckett's no-hopers clambering out of her sack, dustbin or urn and letting language gamely rip.' *The Times*

Lorn Macintyre was born in Taynuilt, Argyll, Scotland, and spent formative years on the Isle of Mull, the inspiration for many of his poems and short stories, including the paranormal tradition of 'second sight,' the ability to foretell the future, which, he says, his family possessed. He researched and scripted television documentaries on cultural subjects for the BBC. He lives in St Andrews with his wife Mary.

His two short-story collections, *Tobermory Days* and *Tobermory Tales* (Argyll Publishing), draw on his life on Mull and his Highland ancestry, as does his poetry collection, *A Snowball in Summer* (Argyll Publishing). His latest short story collection, *Miss Esther Scott's Fancy* (Priormuir Press), reflects his obsessive interest and participation in dancing. His novel *Adoring Venus* (Priormuir Press) is about the passionate affair between a 61-year-old professor of art history and an 18-year-old student at the University of St Andrews.

Websites: www.lornmacintyre.co.uk   www.priormuir-press.co.uk

Manus McManus was born in Dublin in 1959. He has won awards for his fiction and poetry, most recently the Patrick Kavanagh Poetry Award. His work has appeared in *The Irish Times* and *Poetry Ireland*.

Marinella Mezzanotte is an Italian-born ambidextrous vegan who can't imagine living anywhere other than south London. Having done a number of things since the early 1990s with varying degrees of success, she has been working as a life model for the past few years. She loves to translate from Italian into English, even if no one has paid her for it so far, because it makes her a better writer and a better reader. This is the first time that a piece of her fiction has been published in any form. Owing to a bizarre aversion to doing one thing at a time, she is currently working on a novel and a screenplay.

Jennifer Mills is the author of the novels *Gone* and *The Diamond Anchor* and a collection of short stories, *The Rest is Weight*. *The Rest is Weight* was shortlisted for the 2013 Queensland Literary Awards Steele Rudd Award for an Australian Short Story Collection and longlisted for the 2013 Frank O'Connor International Short Story Award. In 2012 Mills was named a Sydney Morning Herald Best Young Australian Novelist for Gone.

Mills' fiction, non-fiction and poetry have been widely published, broadcast, and performed. Mills is currently the fiction editor at *Overland* journal. She lives in a very small town in South Australia.

John Murphy lives and works in Dublin. His book of poetry, *The Book of Water,* was published by Salmon Poetry in 2012 (http://www.salmonpoetry.com/details.php?ID=262&a=223).

He was shortlisted twice for the Hennessy/Sunday Tribune New Irish Writing prize, for short fiction and for poetry. He was also shortlisted for the prestigious Patrick Kavanagh Award. His poetry has been published in many poetry magazines and journals, including *Poetry Ireland Review*, *Cyphers*, *Mimesis*, *The Stony Thursday Book*, *Revival* and *Ambit*. His Bridport shortlisted story, 'Jotunheim', is part of a book of interlinked stories he has just finished writing. He is a computer scientist and academic by profession.

Mai Nardone was raised in Bangkok, Thailand, by an American father and a Thai mother. He is a graduate of Middlebury College and Columbia University's writing program. His fiction has appeared or is forthcoming in *The Kartika Review*, *Slice*, *The Iowa Review* and *The Kenyon Review Online*. He lives in New York City.

Noel O'Regan was born in Co. Kerry, Ireland. He is the recipient of a Leonard A. Koval Memorial Prize and was a prize winner in the Writing Spirit Award. He has been shortlisted for numerous other awards, such as the James Plunkett Award and the Over the Edge New Writer of the Year, as well as being nominated for a 2013 Pushcart Prize. He is short fiction editor for *Five Dials* and is the current Kerry County Council Writer in Residence.

Josephine Rowe is an Australian writer of fiction, poetry and essays. Her stories have previously appeared in *Harvard Review*, *The Iowa Review*, *Five Dials* and *Best Australian Stories*, and in her two collections, *How a Moth Becomes a Boat* (2010, Hunter Publishers) and *Tarcutta Wake* (2012, UQP). She currently lives in Montreal, and is working on a new collection of stories.

Nicholas Ruddock has won prizes in both poetry and fiction from literary journals in Canada. His short story 'How Eunice Got Her Baby' was filmed by the Canadian Film Centre. His 'wildly inventive' novel about poetry and love, *The Parabolist*, was published in February 2010 by Doubleday Canada and was shortlisted for the Toronto Book Award. He lives and works as a family doctor in Guelph.

Stephen Santus was born in Wigan in 1948 and educated at Wigan Grammar School, St Catherine's College Oxford and the University of

Orleans. He taught English in France and Austria before returning to Oxford to teach English in a language school, where he still teaches. He has been writing poetry since 1965. This is his first attempt to find an audience for his work.

Paul Stephenson lives between London and Paris, where he is a researcher in EU politics.

He has published widely in UK magazines, including *Magma*, *The North* and *Poetry London*. He recently won second prize in the Troubadour International Poetry Competition with his poem 'The Teenage Existential'. In 2012/13 he is participating in the Jerwood/Arvon mentorship scheme.

David Steward worked for many years as a maritime lawyer, only to find that the job left no space in his head for writing fiction. Since liberating himself in 2011, he has written short stories and flash fiction, and is working on a novel. He was shortlisted in the Flash Fiction category of the Bridport Prize in 2012. He has published stories in *Flash: the International Short-Story Magazine* in April 2012, three stories in the October 2012 issue and another in April 2013. 'The Gun Cabinet' will be published in the October 2013 issue.

Rebecca Swirsky is a London-based writer with an MA (Distinction) for Writing from Sheffield Hallam University where she was awarded the A.M. Heath Prize for her final MA submission. *Crossing The Line* was awarded third prize in Ilkley's Literature Festival and her fiction has previously been shortlisted for the Bridport Prize and Fish Short Fiction Prize and, this year, shortlisted in the Bridport Flash Fiction category. Rebecca has been awarded a Bursary from The Literary Consultancy through Spread The Word, and her work has been featured in journals and anthologies including *Ambit*, *Matter* and *The Big Issue in the North* anthology. This year, she won the Word Factory apprenticeship for emerging short story writers. Rebecca is currently shaping her collection *Just Something, Just Nothing* with her Word Factory mentor, Stella Duffy. Rebecca used her Bridport Prize money to buy a telescope from a charity shop.

Barry Lee Thompson is an Australian writer. He was born in Liverpool, and now lives in Melbourne. He has won a number of awards for his fiction, and is developing his first collection of short stories. His work has been published in: *Award Winning Australian Writing 2010* (Melbourne Books), *The Sleepers Almanac No. 6* (Sleepers Publishing), *21D Street* (21D) and *21D Anthology I* (Smashwords).

Website: barryleethompson.wordpress.com

Eve Thomson was born in Perth, Scotland and studied painting at the Edinburgh College of Art. Moving to the United States for fifteen years, she taught painting in universities and colleges, brought up her daughter, and exhibited her work both nationally and internationally. She is the recipient of visual arts-related awards and fellowships. In 2006, living again in Edinburgh, and alongside her text-based paintings, she began to write. She received a Scottish Book Trust New Writers Award in 2009, mentored by Alan Bissett, and a Creative Scotland Professional Development Award in 2013. Shortlists include the Orange/Harper's Bazaar Short Story Competition and the Bridport Prize, and work has appeared in the *Bridport Prize 2008* anthology, the Scottish Book Trust's *New Writing from Scotland 2009*, and *Mslexia* issue 58, Jun/Jul/Aug 2013. Her first novel is in final draft.

Shirley Waite took early retirement from local government and moved to Scarborough in 1999. She started a part-time BA in Creative Writing at the University of Hull (Scarborough Campus) having written nothing since her last essay for 'O' level English. She has loved every minute of being a student and is now looking forward to writing 'fun stuff' instead of essays. When she is not writing she is reading, at the theatre or walking by the sea. She self-published on Kindle a non-fiction book *A Menu for Café Church*.

Mary Woodward has published poems in many magazines including *North, Ambit, The London Magazine, Stand,* and *The Shop*. Runner-up, at various times, in the National, Arvon, Strokestown and Troubadour competitions. One pamphlet, *Almost like Talking* (Smith Doorstop '93) and a new collection, *The White Valentine,* due from the Worple Press. She is a member of the Mary Ward poetry group, Queen Square WC1, and lives in St Albans.

Michelle Wright is an Australian writer of short stories and flash fiction. She spent 11 years in Paris and taught for 14 years, before shifting into the community development field. She is passionate about languages, literature and sanitation. Her first short story was shortlisted for the Age Short Story Competition in 2011 and her second, *Maggot*, won in 2012. Her story 'Family Block' won the Grace Marion Wilson Emerging Writers Competition for 2013.

In 2013, she was awarded the inaugural Writers Victoria Templeberg Residential Writing Fellowship which will allow her to spend one month writing short stories in Sri Lanka. She's currently writing more short stories and has started working on a novel.